Macmillan/McGraw-Hill • Glencoe

Grade K

Math Triumphs

Assessment Masters

Macmillan/McGraw-Hill
Glencoe

Send all inquiries to:
Macmillan/McGraw–Hill•Glencoe/McGraw–Hill
8787 Orion Place
Columbus, OH 43240-4027

ISBN: 978-0-07-888242-5
MHID: 0-07-888242-7

Grade K Math Triumphs
Assessment Masters

Printed in the United States of America.

2 3 4 5 6 7 8 9 024 14 13 12 11 10 09

Table of Contents

Section 3: Measurement

Using the Assessment Masters

Math Triumphs Assessment Masters are an important tool in the evaluation of specific areas of student need, appropriate placement, and determining student success and readiness for transitioning back to on-level curriculum. The assessments in this book provide a comprehensive system that allows for diagnostic, formative, and summative assessment.

Diagnostic and Placement Test

The Diagnostic and Placement Test assesses concepts and skills that are presented in an on-level curriculum. The results can be used to determine whether students require intensive intervention, and, if so, what specific content strands students need.

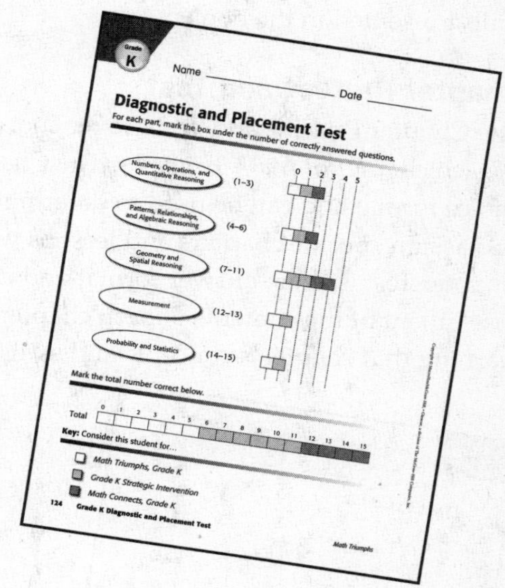
Grade K
Name Date
Diagnostic and Placement Test
For each part, mark the box under the number of correctly answered questions.

Strand	Questions
Numbers, Operations, and Quantitative Reasoning	(1–3)
Patterns, Relationships, and Algebraic Reasoning	(4–6)
Geometry and Spatial Reasoning	(7–11)
Measurement	(12–13)
Probability and Statistics	(14–15)

Mark the total number correct below.
Total 0 1 2 3 4 5 6 7 8 9 10 11 12 13 14 15
Key: Consider this student for...
Math Triumphs, Grade K
Grade K Strategic Intervention
Math Connects, Grade K
124 Grade K Diagnostic and Placement Test
Math Triumphs

The Diagnostic and Placement Tests for Kindergarten through Grade 2 are oral tests and address the content strands: Number, Operations, and Quantitative Reasoning; Measurement; Probability and Statistics; and Mathematical Processes and Tools. The Kindergarten, Grade 1, and Grade 2 tests each contain 15 questions. The Kindergarten and Grade 1 tests require students to follow simple directions in order to answer each question, while the Grade 2 test is multiple choice.

Grades 3–8 share the same format. Each contains 30 multiple-choice questions and addresses the content strands: Number, Operations, and Quantitative Reasoning; Measurement; Probability and Statistics; and Mathematical Processes and Tools.

See page vii for further explanation and instructions for administering and scoring this test.

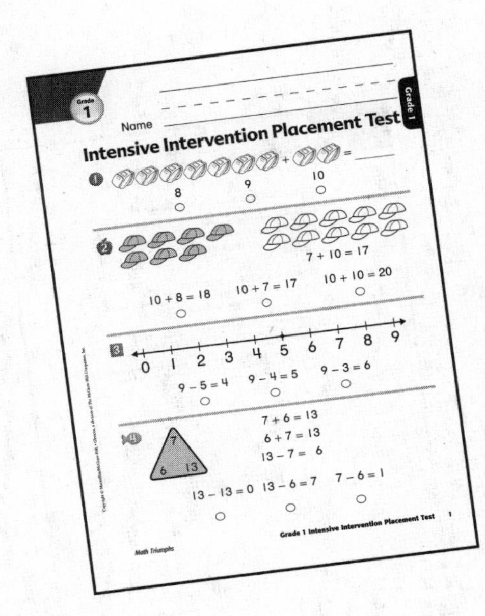
Grade 1
Name
Intensive Intervention Placement Test
1. 8 9 10
2. 10 + 8 = 18 10 + 7 = 17 10 + 10 = 20
3. 0 1 2 3 4 5 6 7 8 9
9 − 5 = 4 9 − 4 = 5 9 − 3 = 6
4. 7 + 6 = 13 6 + 7 = 13 13 − 7 = 6
13 − 13 = 0 13 − 6 = 7 7 − 6 = 1
Math Triumphs
Grade 1 Intensive Intervention Placement Test 1

Intensive Intervention Placement Test

The Intensive Intervention Placement Test covers concepts and skills presented strictly in *Math Triumphs.* (It does not cover on-level content.) This test can determine if a student is in need of intensive intervention, as well as identify specific areas in which a student needs intensive intervention. This assessment provides information about the skills and concepts students are struggling with and then indicates in which specific chapter(s) in *Math Triumphs* students should receive instruction.

Section Pretest and Test

The Section Pretests and Tests cover concepts and skills presented in each of the three books in *Math Triumphs.* The Section Pretest can be used to determine student needs and assign specific chapters and lessons. The Section Test can serve as a summative assessment of the contents of each book to determine student success in learning the concepts and skills presented in the book.

Chapter Pretest and Test

The Chapter Pretests and Tests cover concepts and skills presented in each chapter of *Math Triumphs.* The Chapter Pretest is multiple-choice format and can be used to determine specific student needs and assign specific chapters and lessons within that chapter. The Chapter Test is short-answer format and can serve as a summative assessment of the contents of each chapter to determine student success in learning that chapter's concepts and skills.

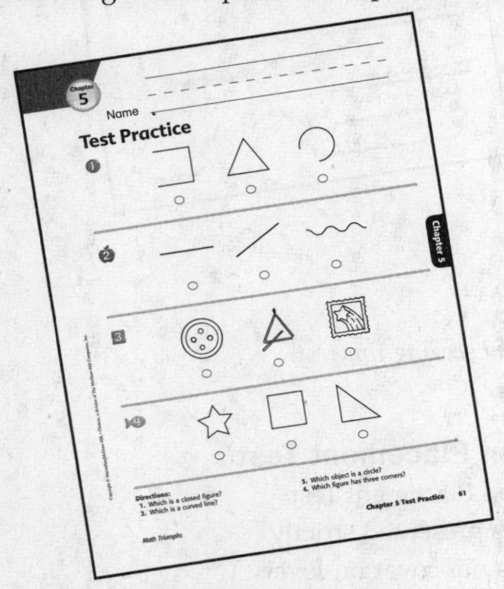
Chapter 5
Name
Test Practice
Directions:
1. Which is a closed figure?
2. Which is a curved line?
3. Which object is a circle?
4. Which figure has three corners?
Math Triumphs
Chapter 5 Test Practice 61

Test Practice

The Test Practice assessment covers concepts and skills presented in each chapter of *Math Triumphs.* It also provides practice for standardized tests by presenting test questions in A, B, C, D standardized-test format. Each chapter's Test Practice can serve as an alternate form of the Chapter Test, providing a summative assessment opportunity.

Performance Assessment

Performance Assessments for each chapter provide an alternate to multiple-choice or fill-in-the-blank assessment. These assessments are multi-step, task-oriented activities that incorporate the concepts and skills learned in the chapter. The activities often involve problem-solving skills and include small projects, games, listening activities, or oral assessments.

In Kindergarten through Grade 3, these performance assessments are led by the teacher. In Grade 4 through Grade 8, these activities can be student self-directed with informal assessment by observation. A scoring rubric is included with each performance assessment.

Answer Key

An Answer Key at the end of this book provides reductions of each student page with answers.

Using the Diagnostic and Placement Test

The **Diagnostic and Placement Test** provides tools to assist teachers in making placement decisions with regard to one of the following on-level, strategic intervention, or intensive intervention resources.

Math Connects
A balanced basal program that provides on-level and strategic intervention instruction.

Math Triumphs
An intensive intervention program for students two or more years behind grade level.

This assessment provides valuable diagnostic information that teachers may also find helpful throughout the school year. The Learning Objectives found before the test provide further information on using these tests as diagnostic tools. These tests are also available in Spanish at macmillanmh.com.

Placement Decisions

In making placement decisions for a student, consider a variety of evidence, such as the student's mathematics grades, classroom observations, teacher recommendations, portfolios of student work, standardized test scores, and placement test scores. Use the results of these placement tests in conjunction with other assessments to determine which mathematics course best fits a student's abilities and needs.

These tests can help determine whether or not students need intervention as well as the level of intervention required. Through strategic intervention, teachers can work with students using on-level content but strategically choose which content strand(s) need further development. Sometimes a student may struggle with a particular strand, but overall the student is able to perform on-level.

Intensive intervention is used with students who are struggling with most or all strands of math content and are unable to work on grade-level. These students will need alternative intervention materials to help meet their needs. These materials, such as the *Math Triumphs* program, offer alternatives that will accelerate achievement in mathematics.

Test Content

These placement tests measure ability, but they are not achievement tests. They cover prerequisite concepts, not every concept found in Macmillan/McGraw-Hill or Glencoe mathematics textbooks or in your state standards.

Mathematics concepts are introduced, developed, and reinforced in consecutive courses. These placement tests measure student mastery of concepts and skills that have been introduced or developed in the student's current mathematics courses and that are further developed in the next course, but that are not developed in the following course.

When to Use the Diagnostic and Placement Test

In most situations, these placement tests are given near the end of the current course in order to help determine student placement for the following year. You can also use these tests in special situations, such as a student transferring into your school mid-year or entering middle school with advanced mathematics ability.

Interpreting Scores

When interpreting scores on the placement tests, consider the student's score on each part, as well as the total score. Scoring Guide Masters before each test can be reproduced and used to record each student's score. A sample of a completed Scoring Guide is shown to the right.

Grade K Name ____________ Date ________

Diagnostic and Placement Test

For each part, mark the box under the number of correctly answered questions.

		0	1	2	3	4	5
Numbers, Operations, and Quantitative Reasoning	(1–3)			X			
Patterns, Relationships, and Algebraic Reasoning	(4–6)				X		
Geometry and Spatial Reasoning	(7–11)		X				
Measurement	(12–13)			X			
Probability and Statistics	(14–15)		X				

Mark the total number correct below.

	0	1	2	3	4	5	6	7	8	9	10	11	12	13	14	15
Total										X						

Key: Consider this student for...

- *Math Triumphs, Grade K*
- *Grade K Strategic Intervention*
- *Math Connects, Grade K*

124 **Grade K Diagnostic and Placement Test** *Math Triumphs*

Sample Score and Placement Analysis

On this sample test, this student scored 2 out of 3 questions correct in Number, Operations, and Quantitative Reasoning; 3 in Patterns, Relationships, and Algebraic Thinking; 1 in Geometry and Spatial Reasoning; 2 in Measurement; and 1 in Probability and Statistics. The total number correct was 9 out of 15. **Note:** There is not a direct correlation between the score for each strand and the total test score. Use the total score for class placement decisions and the score by strand when working on particular objectives.

Sample Analysis

This student scored well in the first two parts of the test, but lower in the remaining sections. If these results are similar to other assessments, this student is likely to need intervention materials and may find the grade-level material too challenging without any intervention. The teacher should also note that the student scored particularly low in the Geometry and Spatial Reasoning. This student may require intensive intervention when these skills are taught.

Using Placement Tests for Diagnostic Purposes

These placement tests also provide valuable diagnostic information for classroom teachers. Reproducible learning-objective charts list the learning objective for each test question and can be found before each test. By marking each question the student answered incorrectly, you can see which objectives the student has not mastered.

Name ______________________

Grade K

Intensive Intervention Placement Test

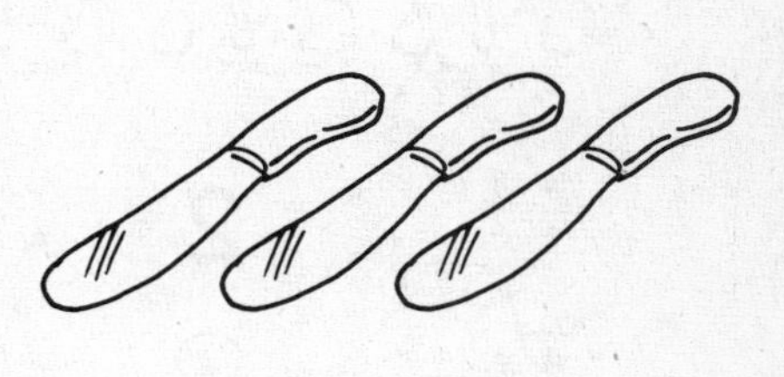

○ ○ ○

6 8 10

○ ○ ○

3

Name ______________________

Intensive Intervention Placement Test

2 ○ 4 ○ 5 ○

5

1 ○ 3 ○ 5 ○

6

2 ○ 3 ○ 4 ○

Name

Intensive Intervention Placement Test

Grade K

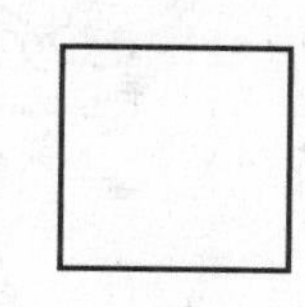

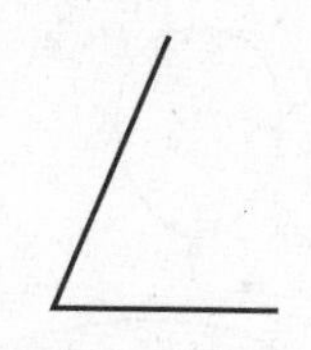

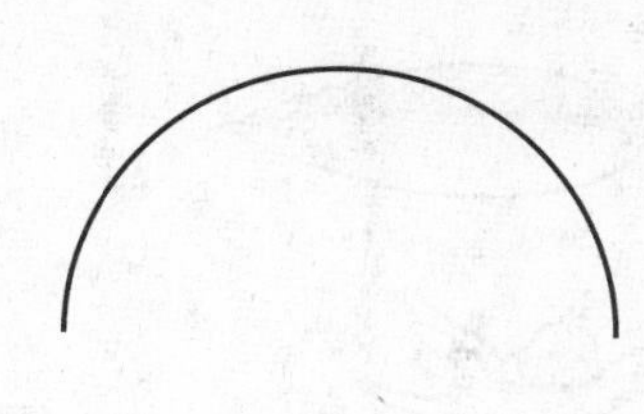

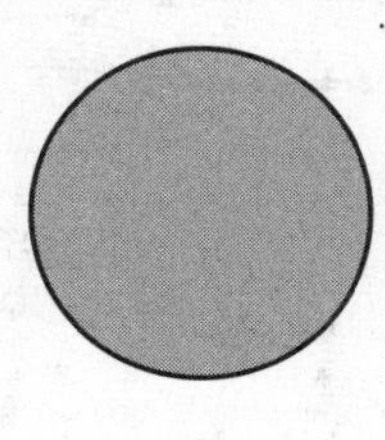

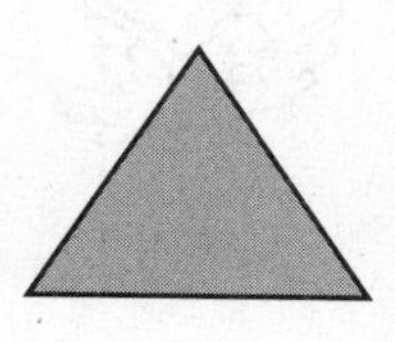

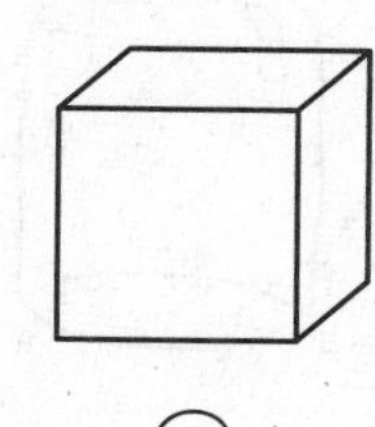

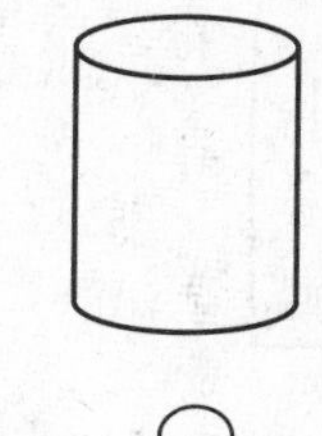

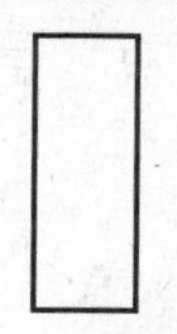

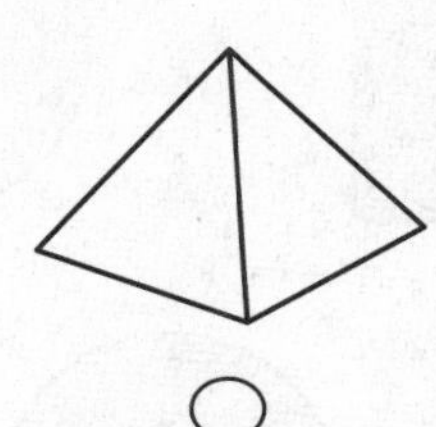

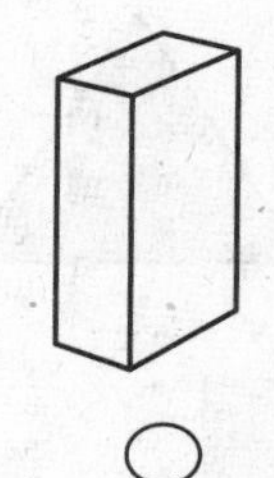

Name

Intensive Intervention Placement Test

12

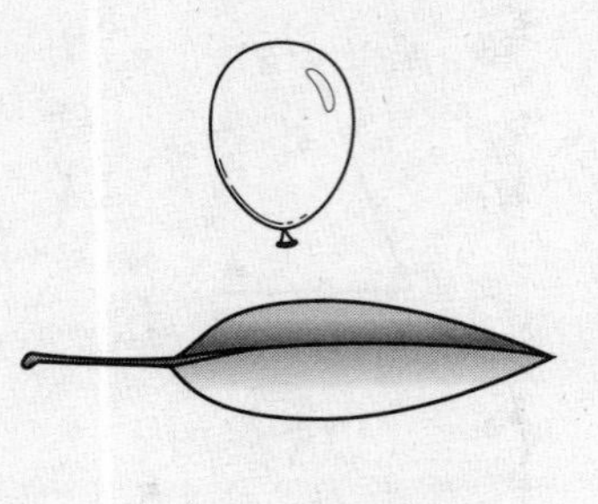
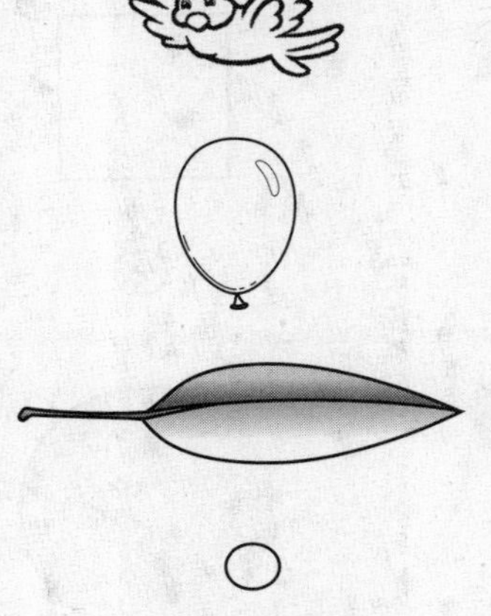
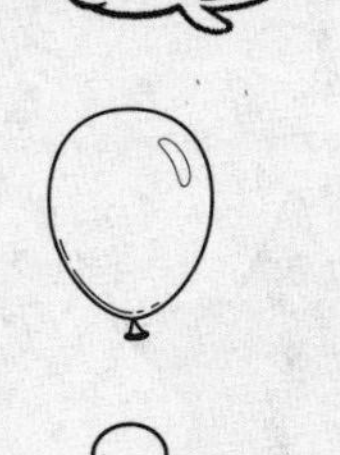

13

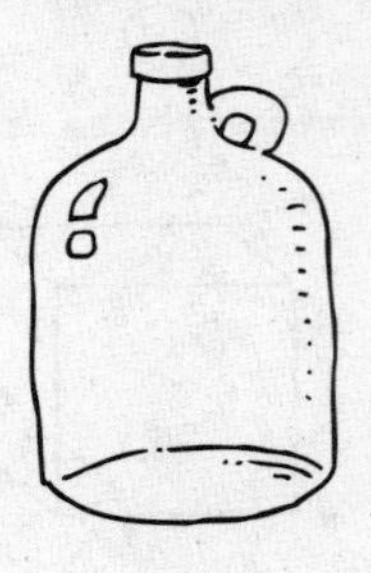

14

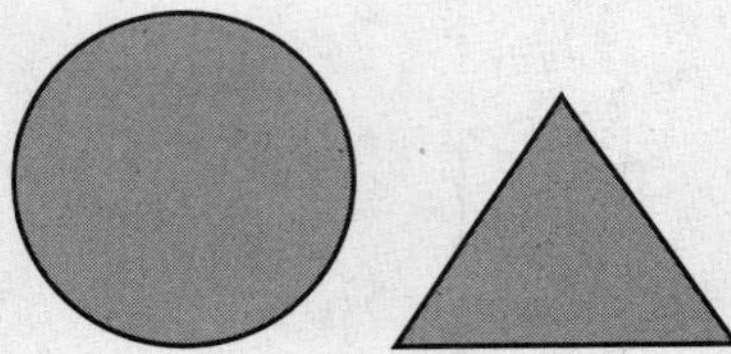

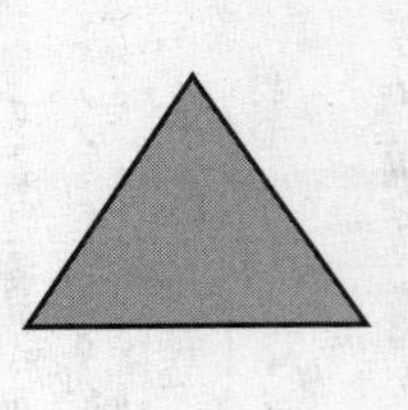

Grade K

Intensive Intervention Placement Test

Scoring Guide and Diagnostic Chart

Students missing Exercise . . .	Have trouble with . . .	Should review . . .
1	Count Objects 0 to 5	Chapter 1, Lesson 1
2	Count Objects 6 to 10	Chapter 1, Lesson 2
3	First, Next, Last	Chapter 2, Lesson 2
4	Sums of 5	Chapter 3, Lesson 3
5	Take Away from 3 and 4	Chapter 4, Lesson 2
6	Take Away from 8	Chapter 4, Lesson 6
7	Open or Closed Figures	Chapter 5, Lesson 1
8	Triangles	Chapter 5, Lesson 4
9	Cylinders	Chapter 6, Lesson 4
10	Rectangular Prisms	Chapter 6, Lesson 5
11	Full or Empty	Chapter 8, Lesson 7
12	Top, Middle, or Bottom	Chapter 7, Lesson 3
13	More and Most	Chapter 9, Lesson 6
14	ABC Patterns	Chapter 10, Lesson 5

Teacher Directions

Read the following directions to students before they begin. Then, read each question followed by a pause to allow students time to work and choose an answer.

- **Write your name at the top of the page.**
- **I am going to read each question to you. Listen carefully before you choose an answer.**

1. Count the objects. Which is a group of five?
2. How many plates are there?
3. Which animal is first in line?

- **Turn the page over.**

4. Three dogs are in the park. Then two more dogs walk into the park. How many dogs are in the park in all?
5. Four frogs were in the pond. Three hop away. How many frogs are left in the pond?
6. Eight cats were in the yard. Five cats run away. How many cats are in the yard now?

- **Go to the next page.**

7. Which is a closed figure?
8. Which figure has three corners?
9. Which figure is a cylinder?
10. Look at the rectangle. Which has a rectangle as one of its faces?
11. Which cup is empty?

- **Turn the page over.**

12. Which group shows the bird in the middle?
13. Look at the items. Which item holds the most?
14. Look at the pattern. Which figure comes next?

Name ______________________

Section Pretest (Chapters 1–4)

1

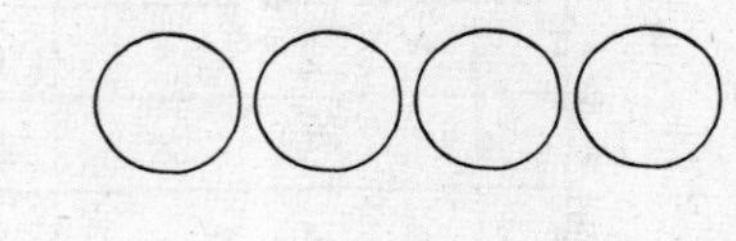

2

3 4 5

3

Name ______________________

Section Pretest (Chapters 1–4)

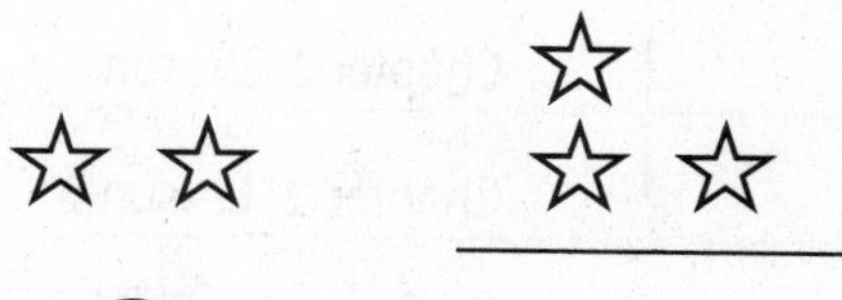

2 ____ 4 5

2 3 6

○ ○ ○

1 2 3

○ ○ ○

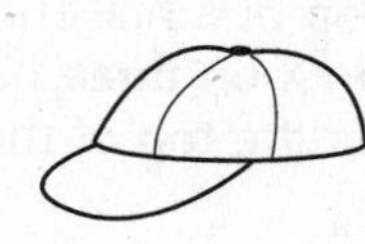
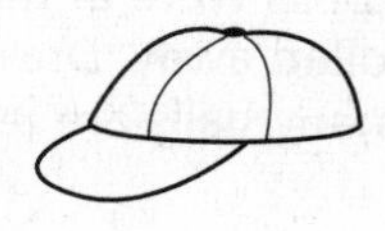
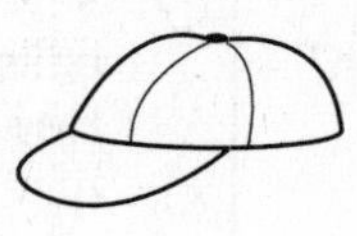
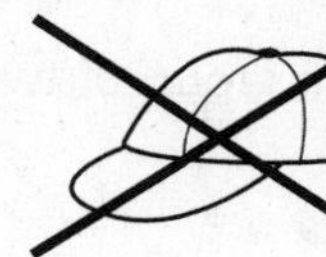

2 7 3

○ ○ ○

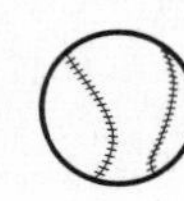
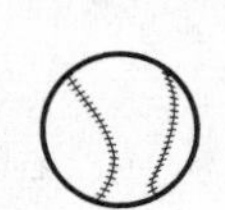
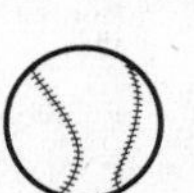

4 1 5

Section Pretest (Chapters 1–4)
Scoring Guide and Diagnostic Chart

Students missing Exercise . . .	Have trouble with . . .	Should review . . .
1	Count Objects 0 to 5	Chapter 1, Lesson 1
2	Numbers 4 and 5	Chapter 1, Lesson 7
3	First, Next, Last	Chapter 2, Lesson 2
4	More Number Patterns	Chapter 2, Lesson 8
5	Sums of 3 and 4	Chapter 3, Lesson 2
6	Take Away From 5	Chapter 4, Lesson 3
7	Take Away From 7	Chapter 4, Lesson 5

Teacher Directions

Read the following directions to students before they begin. Then, read each question followed by a pause to allow students time to work and choose an answer.

- **Write your name at the top of the page.**
- **I am going to read each question to you. Listen carefully before you choose an answer.**

1. Count the objects. Which is a group of two?
2. How many hats are there?
3. Which animal is last in line?

- **Turn the page over.**

4. Look for a pattern. Which number is missing?
5. Mave has two peanuts. Alex gives her one peanut. How many peanuts does Mave have in all?
6. There were five caps on a shelf. Adam took two caps off the shelf. How many caps are left on the shelf?
7. Seven balls were at the top of a hill. Three balls rolled away. Draw an X on three balls. How many balls are left at the top of the hill?

Chapter 1

Name ______________________

Chapter Pretest

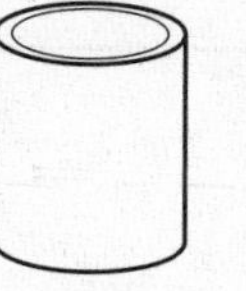
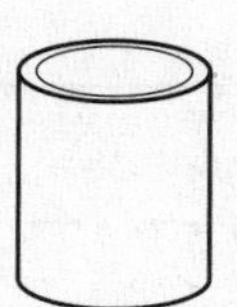

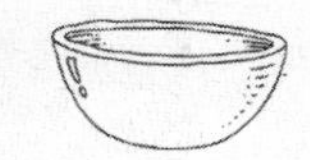

3

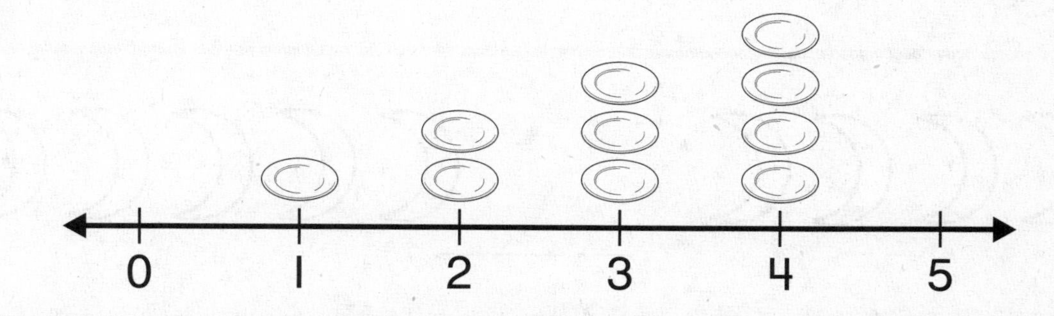

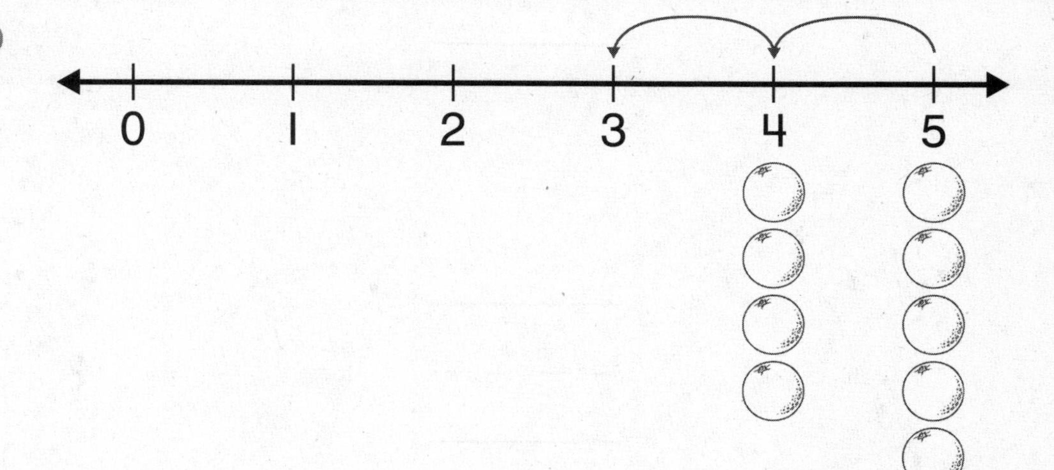

Directions:

1. Draw Xs on 4 cans.
2. Circle 6 bowls.
3. Draw the number of plates that come next.
4. Count backward from 5. Draw the number of oranges that come next.

Chapter 1

Name

Chapter Pretest

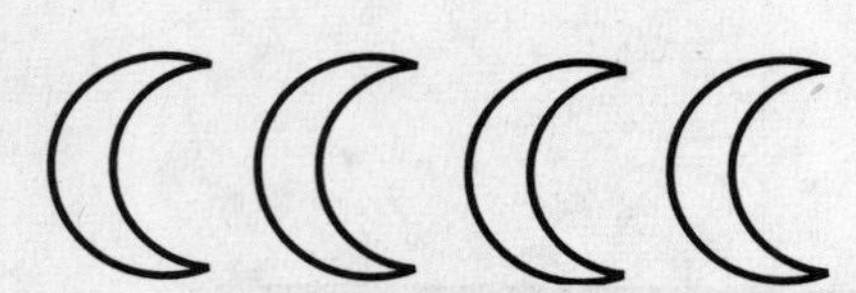

Directions:

5. How many stars are there? Write the number three times.
6. Count the clouds. Write the number three times.
7. Circle the group of 4. Write the number.
8. Draw 7 suns. Write the number.

Chapter Pretest

Scoring Guide and Diagnostic Chart

Students missing Exercise . . .	Have trouble with . . .	Should review . . .
1	Count Objects 0 to 5	Chapter 1, Lesson 1
2	Count Objects 6 to 10	Chapter 1, Lesson 2
3	Count Forward	Chapter 1, Lesson 3
4	Count Backward	Chapter 1, Lesson 4
5	Numbers 0 and 1	Chapter 1, Lesson 5
6	Numbers 2 and 3	Chapter 1, Lesson 6
7	Numbers 4 and 5	Chapter 1, Lesson 7
8	Numbers 6 to 10	Chapter 1, Lesson 8

Chapter 1

Name

Chapter Test

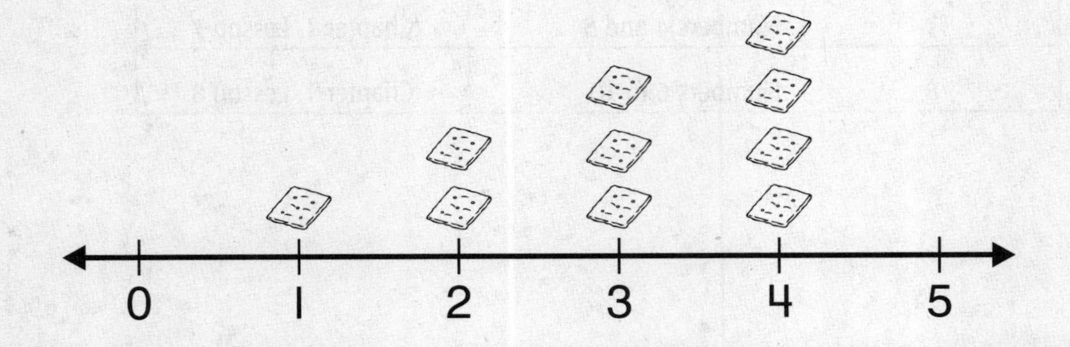

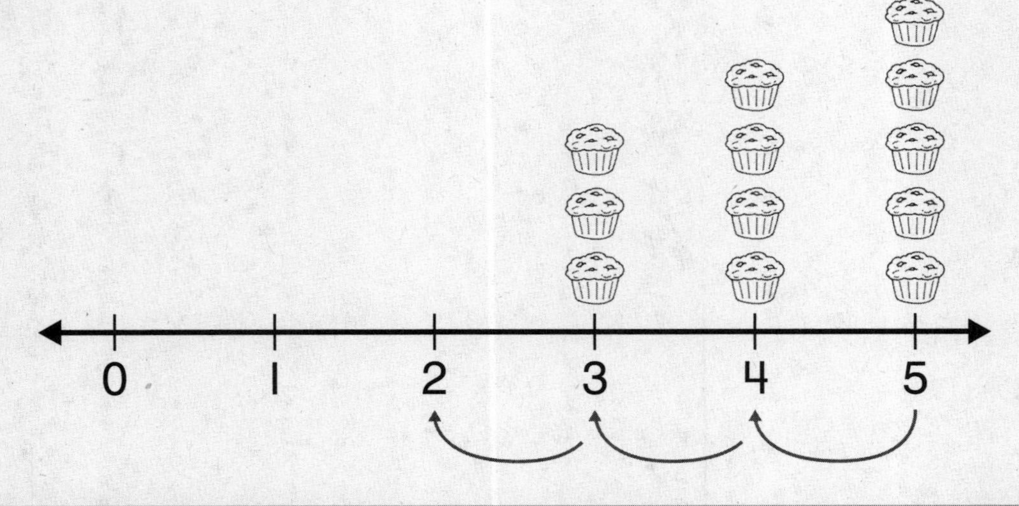

Directions:

1. Draw Xs on 3 pies.
2. Circle 7 eggs.
3. Draw the number of crackers that come next.
4. Count backward from 5. Draw the number of muffins that come next.

Name

Chapter Test

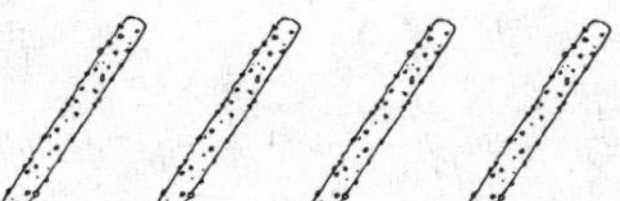
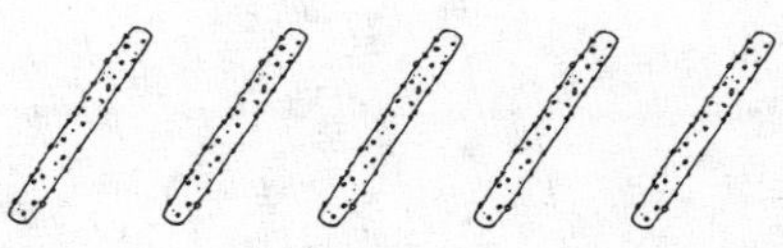

Directions:

5. How many tacos are there? Write the number three more times.
6. Count the pizzas. Write the number three times.
7. Circle the group of 5. Write the number.
8. Draw 8 apples. Write the number.

Chapter 1

Chapter Test

Scoring Guide and Diagnostic Chart

Students missing Exercise . . .	Have trouble with . . .	Should review . . .
1	Count Objects 0 to 5	Chapter 1, Lesson 1
2	Count Objects 6 to 10	Chapter 1, Lesson 2
3	Count Forward	Chapter 1, Lesson 3
4	Count Backward	Chapter 1, Lesson 4
5	Numbers 0 and 1	Chapter 1, Lesson 5
6	Numbers 2 and 3	Chapter 1, Lesson 6
7	Numbers 4 and 5	Chapter 1, Lesson 7
8	Numbers 6 to 10	Chapter 1, Lesson 8

Name ______________________

Test Practice

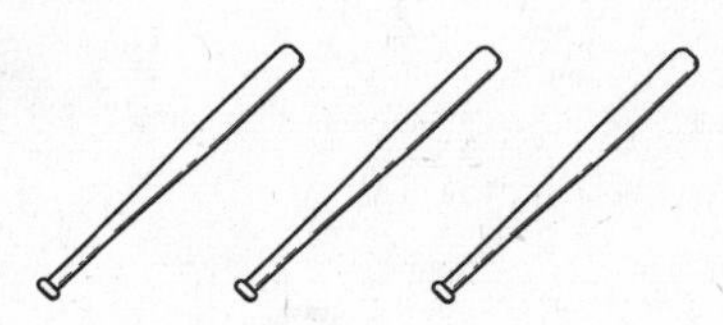

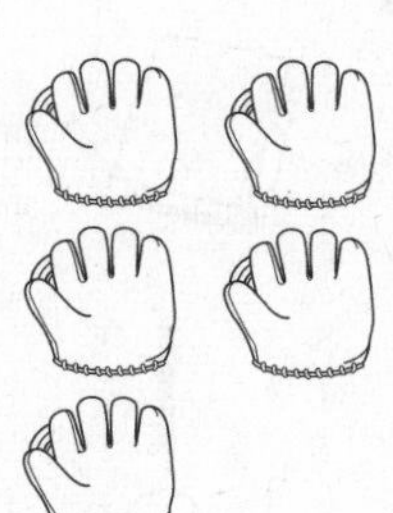

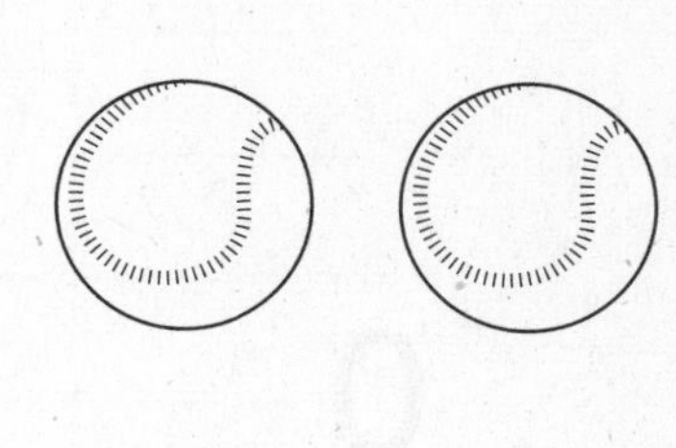

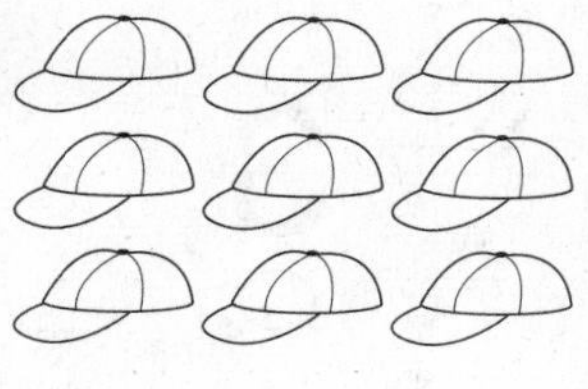

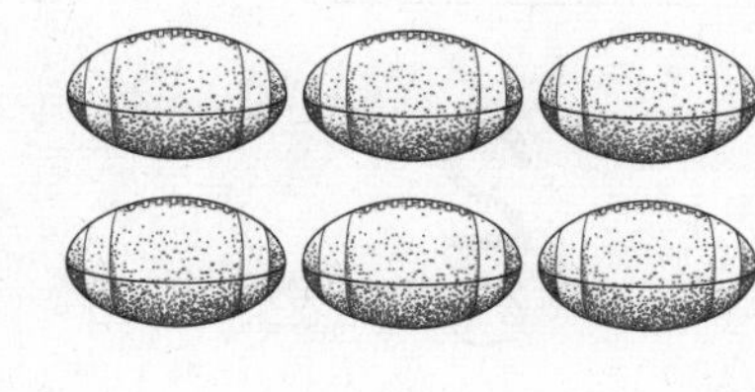

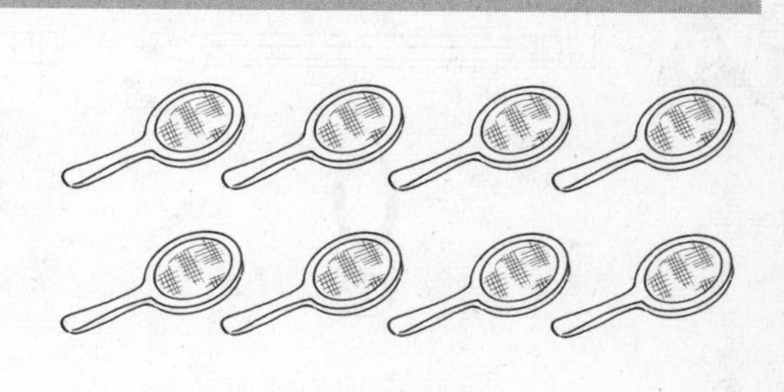

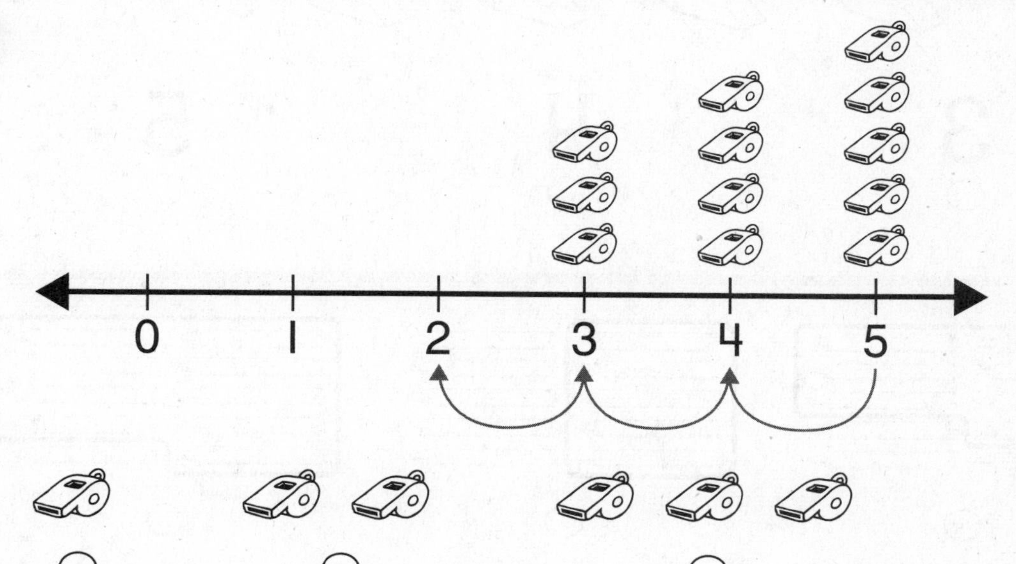

Directions:

1. Look at the objects. Which is a group of 5?
2. Look at the objects. Which is a group of 9?
3. Start at 5 and count backward. Which picture shows the number of whistles that come next?

Chapter 1

Name

Test Practice

0 1 2

 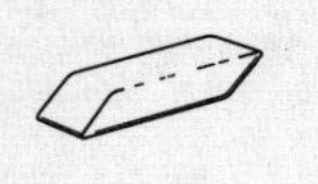 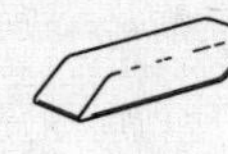

0 2 3

3 4 5

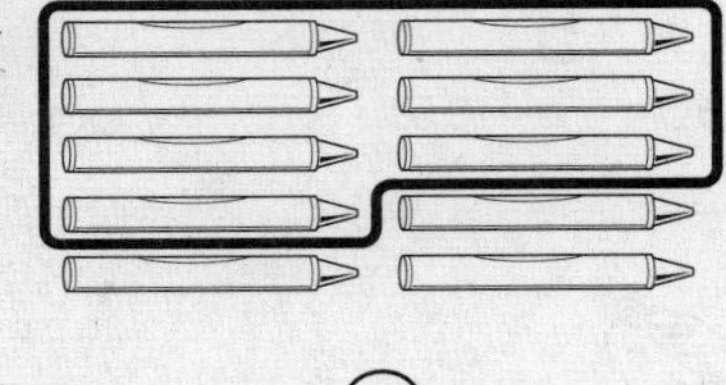 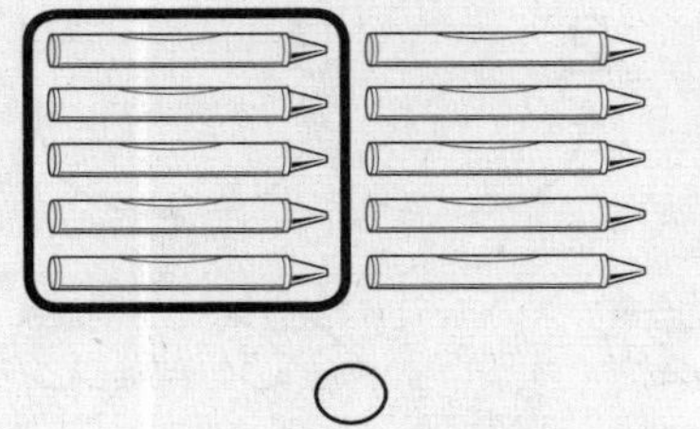 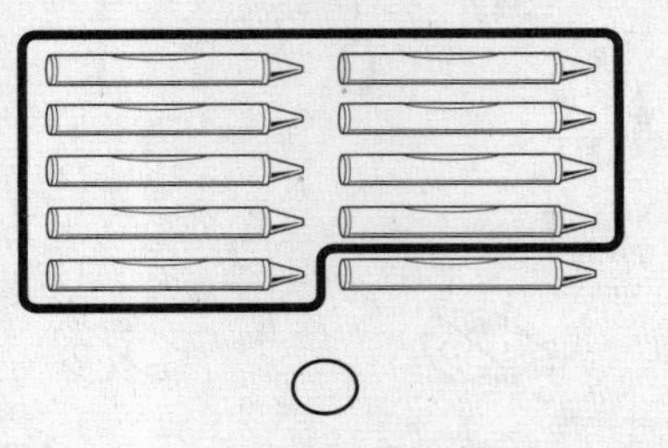

Directions:

4. How many books are there?
5. How many pencils are there?
6. How many erasers are there?
7. Which shows a circle around a group of 7 crayons?

Chapter 1

Performance Assessment

STUDENT TASK: Use numeral cards to count objects and to read and trace numerals.

Teacher Preparation/Instructions:

- Lay out craft sticks in groups as follows: 0, 1, 2, 3, 4, 5, 6, 7, 8, 9, 10.
- Set each group in a row on a sheet of white paper. (For the numeral zero, use a blank sheet of paper.)
- Place numeral cards for numerals 0–10 in either a bag or a box.
- Provide several sets of traceable numerals on lined paper, one numeral to a page.

ONE WAY:

Lead students through the following steps:

- Tell students they will be helping a make-believe builder build a house. Explain that each student will help the builder by counting the number of sticks the builder needs.
- Have students choose numerals from a bag to see how many sticks the builder needs.
- After each student chooses a numeral, have the student read it aloud.
- Allow the student time to locate and to point to the group of sticks that matches the numeral. Then, have the student count the sticks in the group aloud.
- Give the student a sheet of lined paper. Have the student say the numeral and then trace it on the sheet of paper.

ANOTHER WAY:

- Instead of laying out the sticks in groups, place ten sticks on a table.
- Have students pull numerals from the bag and then set apart the correct number of sticks.
- All other aspects of the activity remain the same.

Chapter 1

Performance Assessment Teacher's Notes

Target Skills

- Count objects 0–10.
- Read numerals 0–10.
- Trace numerals 0–10.

Task Description

Students will count objects and read and trace numerals.

Teacher Notes

- Prior to beginning the activity, review counting by chorally counting the number of sticks in each group, including the blank sheet of paper.
- Model an example before students begin to play.
- After all ten numeral cards have been pulled from the bag, return them to the bag for continued play.

Scoring Rubric	
Score	Explanation
3	Students demonstrate an efficient strategy that enables them to solve the problem completely. Students will: • count the number of sticks in the group correctly. • correctly read numerals. • correctly trace numerals.
2	Students demonstrate a strategy that enables them to solve the problem correctly. The strategy is disorganized or less efficient. Students may: • have some difficulty in reading the numeral but locate the correct group. • read the numeral and locate the correct group but have difficulty in tracing the numeral.
1	Students demonstrate a confused strategy that leads to difficulty in solving the problem. Most answers are incorrect, but students demonstrate knowledge of at least one concept. Students may: • be unable to read or trace the numeral but able to locate the correct group. • be unable to read the numeral or locate the correct group but able to correctly trace the numeral after teacher prompting.

Name ______________________

Chapter Pretest

1 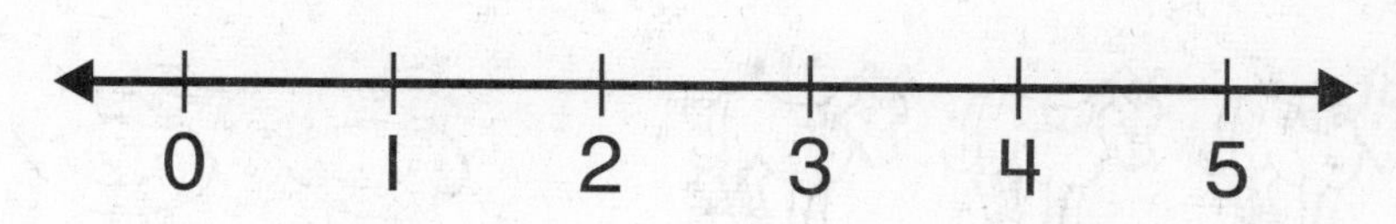

2 

3 

Directions:

1. Circle the number that comes just before 3.
2. Circle the duck that is last in line.
3. Circle the second bird.
4. Circle the fourth animal.
5. Circle the group with the same number of animals as the group of chickens.

Chapter 2

Name ____________________

Chapter Pretest

7 6 ____ 4 3

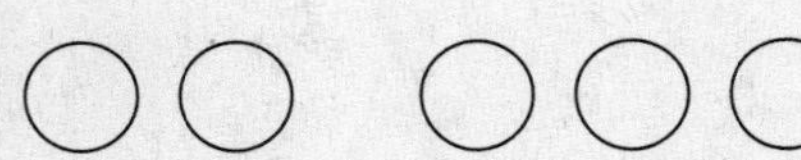
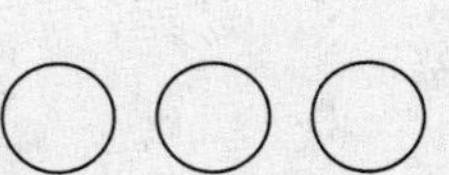
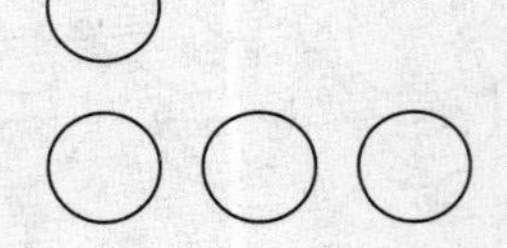

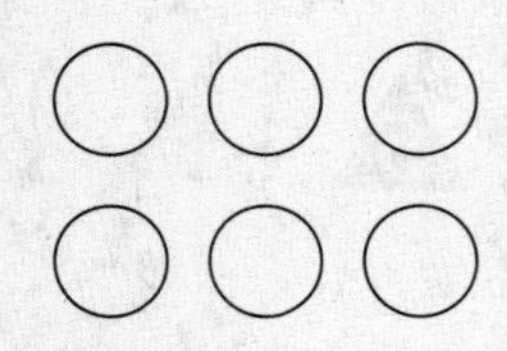

Directions:

6. Draw an X on the group that is less than the other.
7. Look for a pattern. Write the missing number.
8. Look for a pattern. Draw a picture in the box for the missing number.

Chapter 2

Chapter Pretest

Scoring Guide and Diagnostic Chart

Students missing Exercise . . .	Have trouble with . . .	Should review . . .
1	Before and After	Chapter 2, Lesson 1
2	First, Next, Last	Chapter 2, Lesson 2
3	Second and Third	Chapter 2, Lesson 3
4	Fourth and Fifth	Chapter 2, Lesson 4
5	Equal Sets	Chapter 2, Lesson 5
6	Greater Than and Less Than	Chapter 2, Lesson 6
7	More Number Patterns	Chapter 2, Lesson 8
8	Growing Number Patterns	Chapter 2, Lesson 7

Chapter 2

Name ____________________

Chapter Test

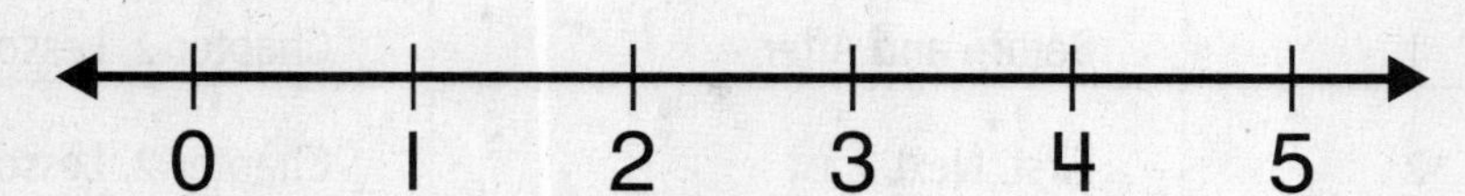

Directions:

1. Circle the number that comes just before 2.
2. Circle the monkey that is first in line.
3. Circle the third lion.
4. Circle the fifth elephant.

Name ______________

Chapter Test

9 8 7 ____ 5

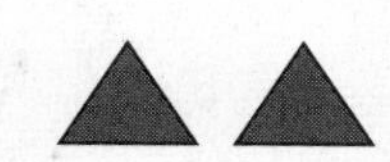

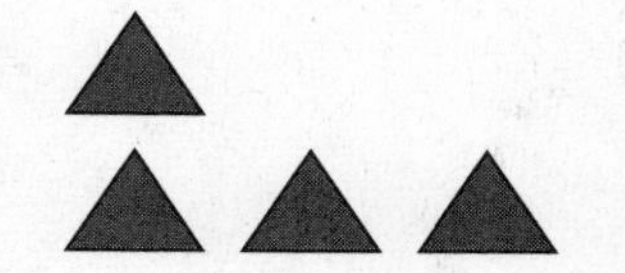

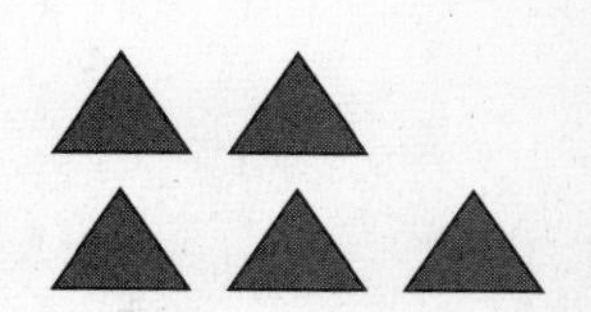

Directions:

5. Circle the group with the same number of animals as the group of zebras.
6. Draw an X on the group that is greater than the other.
7. Look for a pattern. Write the missing number.
8. Look for a pattern. Draw a picture in the box for the missing number.

Chapter 2

Chapter Test

Scoring Guide and Diagnostic Chart

Students missing Exercise . . .	Have trouble with . . .	Should review . . .
1	Before and After	Chapter 2, Lesson 1
2	First, Next, Last	Chapter 2, Lesson 2
3	Second and Third	Chapter 2, Lesson 3
4	Fourth and Fifth	Chapter 2, Lesson 4
5	Equal Sets	Chapter 2, Lesson 5
6	Greater Than and Less Than	Chapter 2, Lesson 6
7	More Number Patterns	Chapter 2, Lesson 8
8	Growing Number Patterns	Chapter 2, Lesson 7

Name

Test Practice

1

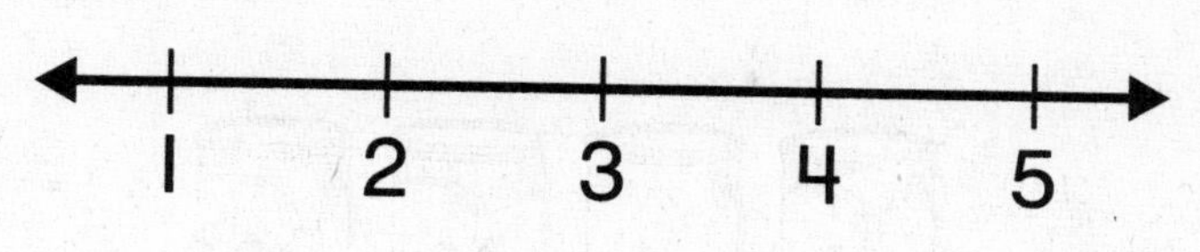

2 ○ 4 ○ 5 ○

2

○ ○ ○

3

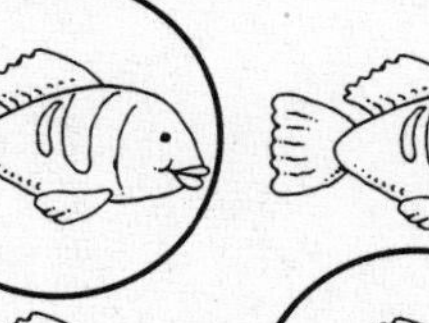

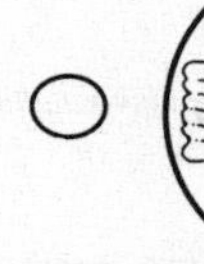

Directions:
1. Which number comes just after 3?
2. The animals are walking toward the plant. Which animal is first in line?
3. Which shows a circle around the third fish?

Chapter 2

Name

Test Practice

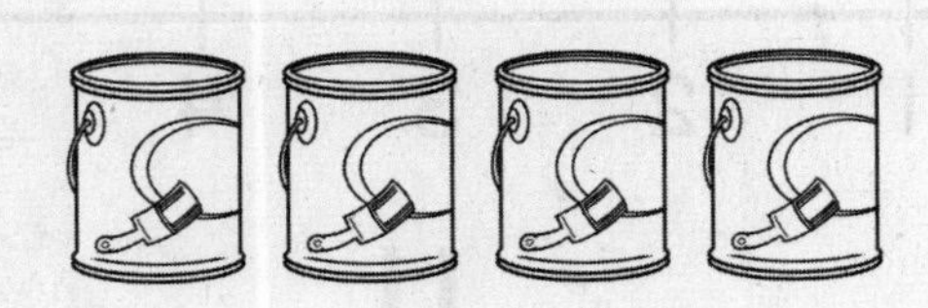

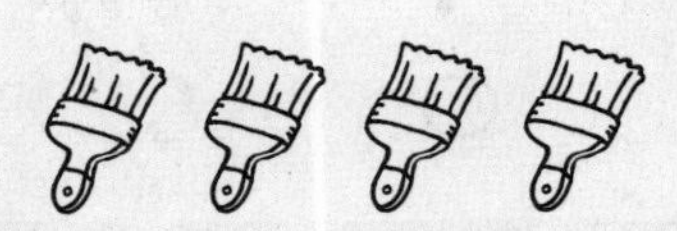

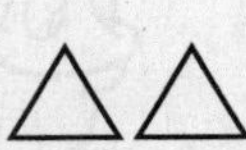

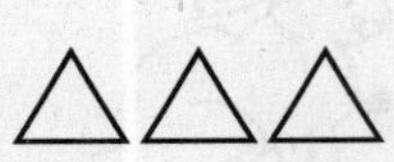

1 2 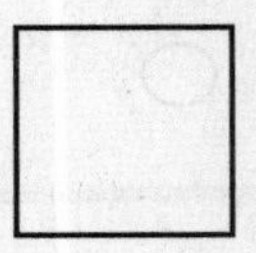 4 5

1 3 7

Directions:

4. Which group of paint brushes is greater than the group of paint cans?

5. Look for a pattern. Which number is missing?

Performance Assessment

STUDENT TASK: Identify animals by position: *first, last, next, second, third, fourth, fifth, before*, and *after*.

Teacher Preparation/Instructions:

- Place six different kinds of plush or plastic animals in a row, all facing in the same direction.
- At the head of the row, place a box.

For example:

- Tell students they will be helping animals prepare for a parade into the park. Point to the box and ask students to make believe it is the park. Explain that the animals must be lined up in the correct order, as well as facing the park.
- Ask the questions below and have students respond through this sentence frame for 1–7.
  The ________ is ________ in line.
- Model this sentence frame for responses to 8–9:
  The ________ is ________ the ________.

1. Which animal is first in line? (cat)
2. Which animal is next in line? (rabbit)
3. Which animal is last in line? (frog)
4. Which animal is second in line? (rabbit)
5. Which animal is fourth in line? (duck)
6. Which animal is third in line? (dog)
7. Which animal is fifth in line? (horse)
8. Which animal is before the duck? (dog)
9. Which animal is after the cat? (rabbit)

Chapter 2

Performance Assessment Teacher's Notes

Target Skills

- Identify objects by position: *first, last, next, second, third, fourth, fifth, before,* and *after*.

Task Description

Students will identify animals in the following positions on a line: first, last, next, second, third, fourth, and fifth. Students will also identify animals that are before and after specified animals in the line.

Teacher Notes

- Model each sentence frame just before its first use.
- You may extend play by changing the order of the animals, putting the "park" on the other side of the line, and turning the animals to face the park.

Scoring Rubric	
Score	Explanation
3	Students demonstrate an efficient strategy that enables them to solve the problem completely. Students will: • correctly point out each animal in the specified position. • correctly identifies the position in a complete oral sentence.
2	Students demonstrate a strategy that enables them to solve the problem correctly. The strategy is disorganized or less efficient. Students may: • use cardinal numbers rather than ordinal numbers in the sentence frame. • have to place their hands on the animals and name them while thinking aloud prior to giving a response.
1	Students demonstrate a confused strategy that leads to difficulty in solving the problem. Most answers are incorrect, but chlidren demonstrate knowledge of at least one concept. Students may: • be unable to identify the correct animal. • be unable to complete an oral sentence without teacher prompting.

Chapter 3

Name

Chapter Pretest

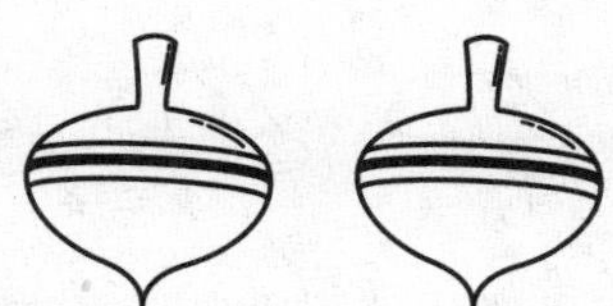

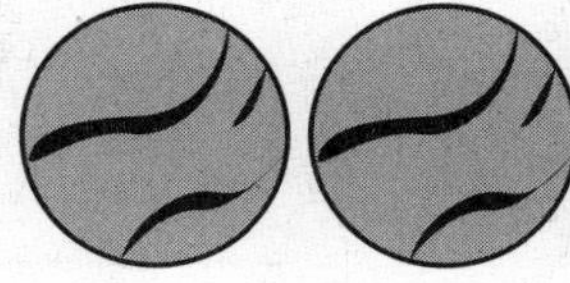

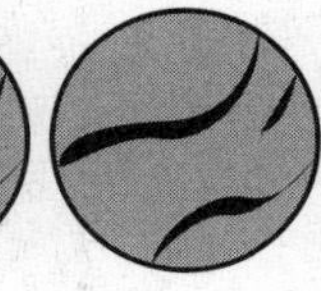

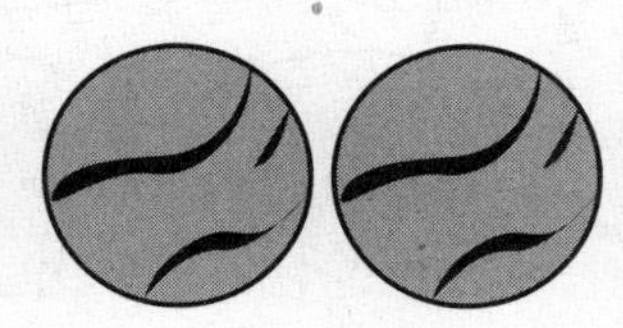

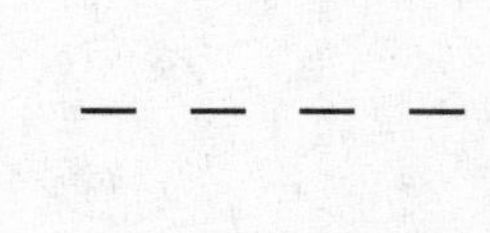

Directions:

1. José has 0 crayons. His teacher gives him 1 crayon. How many crayons does José have in all?
2. Gina has 2 tops. She gets 2 more tops. How many tops does she have in all?
3. There are 2 dolls in a box. Then, Pat puts 1 teddy bear in the box. How many items are in the box in all?
4. Iman has 3 marbles. She finds 2 more. How many marbles does Iman have in all?

Chapter 3

Name

Chapter Pretest

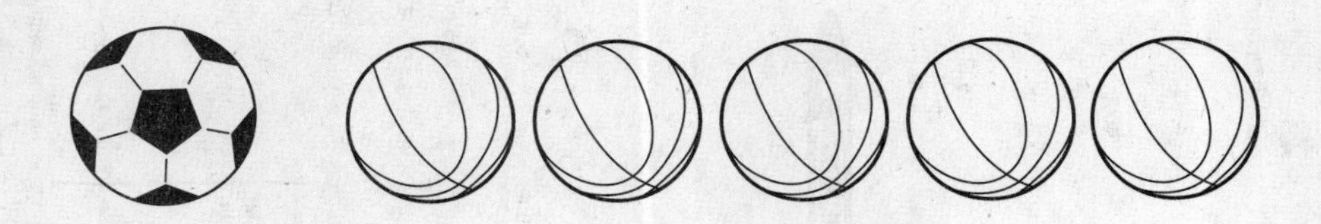

6

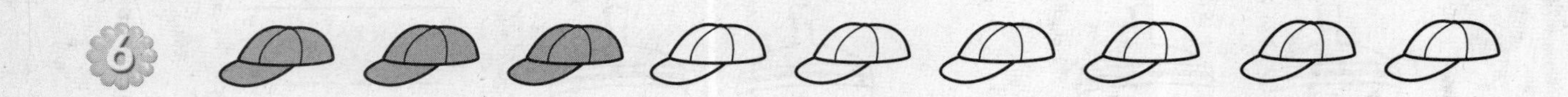

7

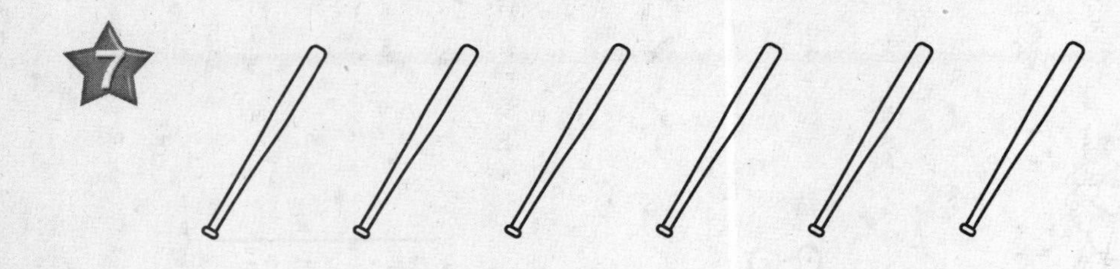

8

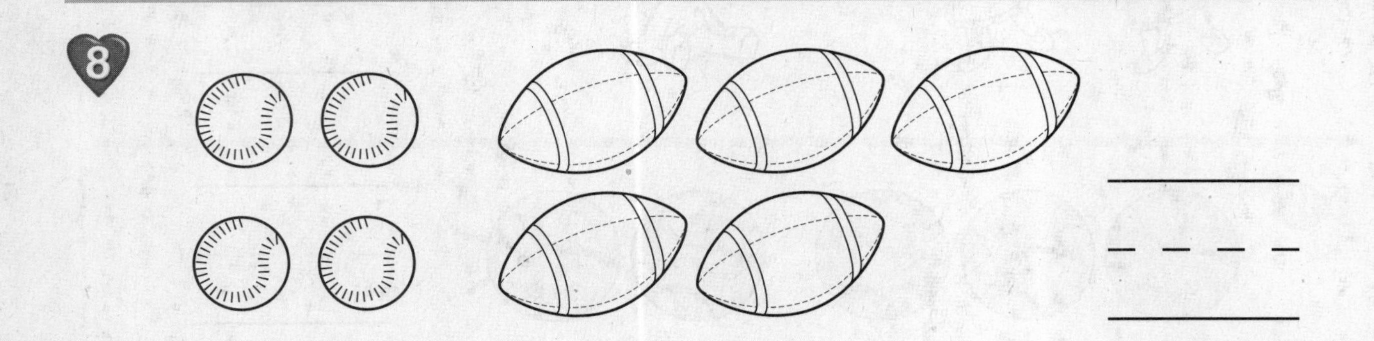

Directions:

5. How many soccer balls are there? How many basketballs are there? How many balls are there in all?
6. Don has 3 caps. Color more caps to show 7 caps in all.
7. Draw enough bats to have 8 in all.
8. Rula takes 4 baseballs outside. The teacher takes 5 footballs outside. How many balls do Rula and the teacher take outside in all?

Chapter Pretest

Scoring Guide and Diagnostic Chart

Students missing Exercise . . .	Have trouble with . . .	Should review . . .
1	Sums of 1 and 2	Chapter 3, Lesson 1
2	Sums of 3 and 4	Chapter 3, Lesson 2
3	Sums of 3 and 4	Chapter 3, Lesson 2
4	Sums of 5	Chapter 3, Lesson 3
5	Sums of 6	Chapter 3, Lesson 4
6	Sums of 7	Chapter 3, Lesson 5
7	Sums of 8	Chapter 3, Lesson 6
8	Sums of 9	Chapter 3, Lesson 7

Chapter 3

Name

Chapter Test

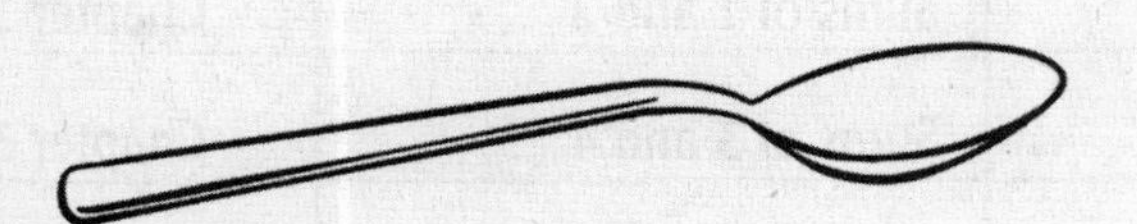

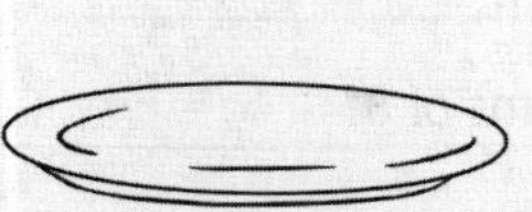

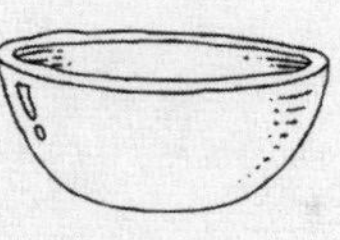

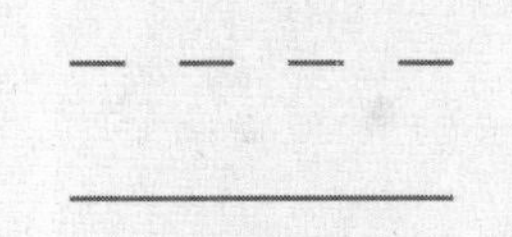

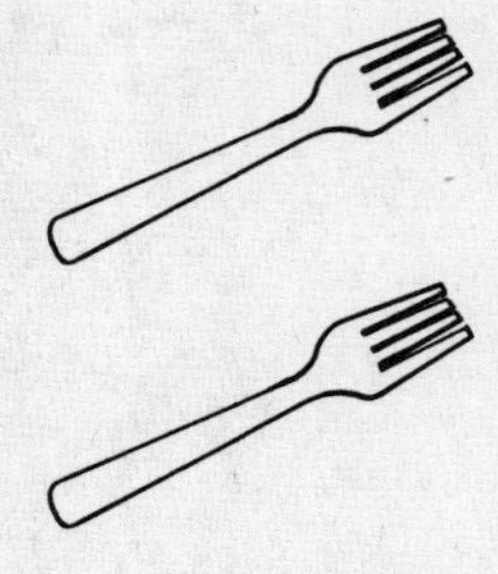

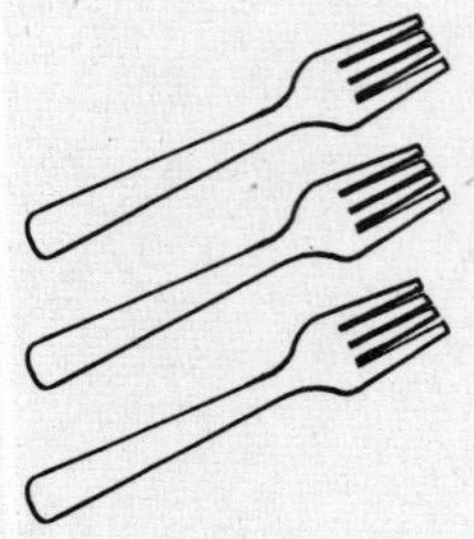

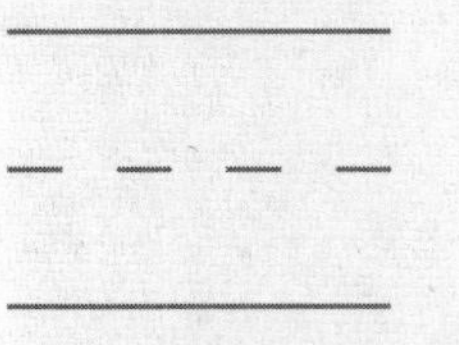

Directions:

1. Diane has 0 spoons. Her mom gives her 1 spoon. How many spoons does Diane have in all?
2. Jamil puts 2 plates on the table. Then, he puts 1 more plate on the table. How many plates does Jamil put on the table in all?
3. There are 2 cups in the sink. Lee puts 2 bowls in the sink. How many items are in the sink in all?
4. Jack gets 2 forks. Then, he gets 3 more. How many forks does Jack have in all?

Chapter 3

Name

Chapter Test

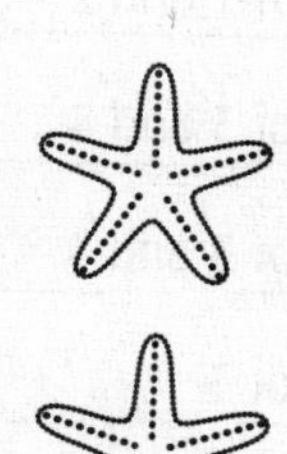

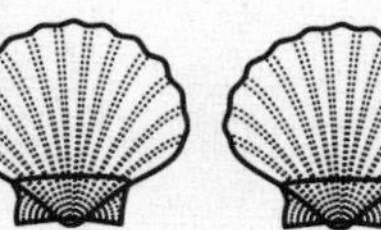

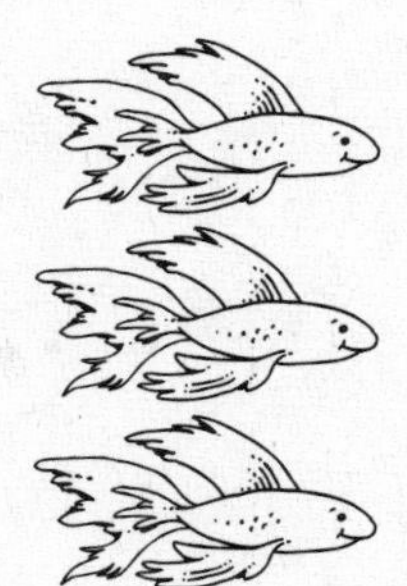
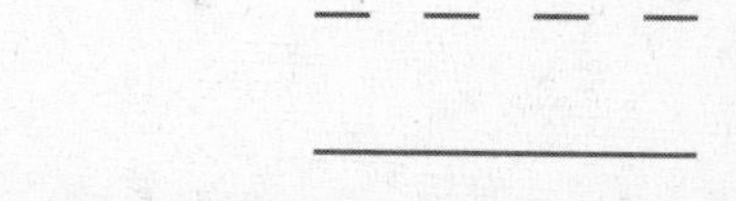

Directions:

5. How many seahorses are there? How many starfish are there? How many animals are there in all?
6. Juan has 2 shells. Color more shells so he has 7 shells in all.
7. Draw enough suns to have 8 in all.
8. Cheena sees 6 fish. Joe sees 3 fish. How many fish do Cheena and Joe see in all?

Chapter 3

Chapter Test

Scoring Guide and Diagnostic Chart

Students missing Exercise . . .	Have trouble with . . .	Should review . . .
1	Sums of 1 and 2	Chapter 3, Lesson 1
2	Sums of 3 and 4	Chapter 3, Lesson 2
3	Sums of 3 and 4	Chapter 3, Lesson 2
4	Sums of 5	Chapter 3, Lesson 3
5	Sums of 6	Chapter 3, Lesson 4
6	Sums of 7	Chapter 3, Lesson 5
7	Sums of 8	Chapter 3, Lesson 6
8	Sums of 9	Chapter 3, Lesson 7

Chapter 3

Name

Test Practice

1    

3 ○ 4 ○ 5 ○

2    

4 ○ 5 ○ 6 ○

5 ○ 6 ○ 7 ○

Directions:

1. Laney sees 2 ducks. Then, she sees 2 more ducks. How many ducks did Laney see in all?
2. Mia walked 4 pigs to the pen. Then, she walked 2 more pigs to the pen. How many pigs went to the pen in all?
3. Count the number of cows in each group. How many cows are there in all?

Chapter 3

Name ______________________

Test Practice

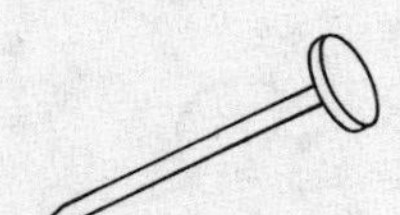
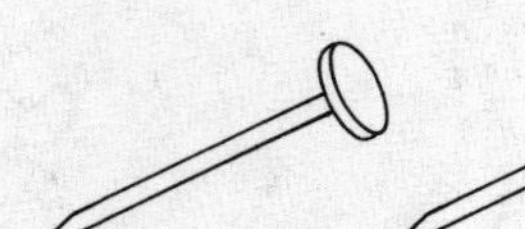

2 ○ 3 ○  ○

7 ○ 8 ○  ○

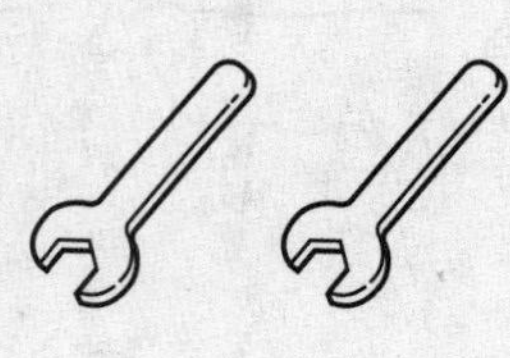

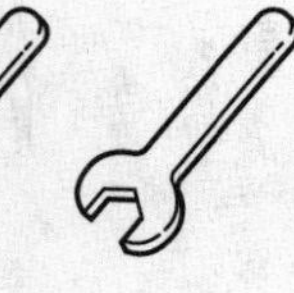

6 ○ 7 ○ 8 ○

Directions:

4. Kevin used 1 nail. Then, he used 2 more nails. How many nails did Kevin use in all?

5. Dad said 3 screws fell on the floor. Then, 6 more screws fell on the floor. How many screws fell on the floor in all?

6. Count the number of tools in each group. How many tools are there in all?

Chapter 3

Performance Assessment

STUDENT TASK: Use number cards and counters to model addition sentences.

Teacher Preparation/Instructions:

- Create two stacks of numeral cards with cards placed facedown. In one stack, include numeral cards 0–5. In the other stack, include numeral cards 1–4.
- Provide counters and mats.

Lead students through the following steps:

- The student draws a card from one stack, identifies the numeral aloud, and puts the card faceup on the mat.
- The student places the correct number of counters below the card.
- The student draws a card from the other stack, identifies the numeral aloud, and places the card faceup on the mat.
- The student puts the correct number of counters below the card.
- Provide the following sentence frame and have the student echo while orally filling in the correct numerals.

I have ______ counters and ______ counters, so I have ______ counters in all.

For example:

I have three counters and two counters, so I have five counters in all.

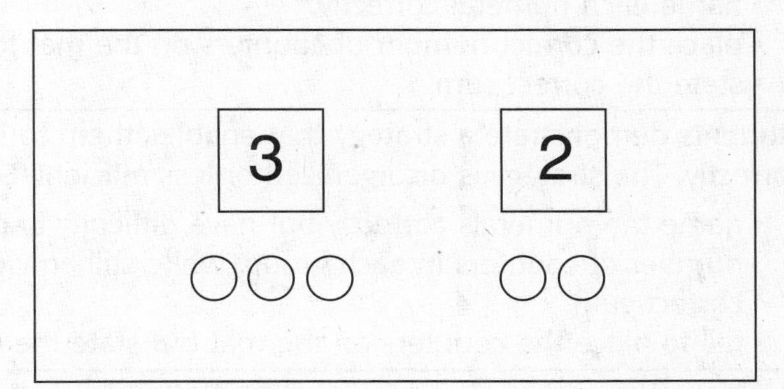

Chapter 3

Chapter 3

Performance Assessment Teacher's Notes

Target Skills

- Work with sums of 1–9.

Task Description

Students will choose two number cards from two different stacks. Students will place the cards on a mat with the appropriate number of counters to represent the number on each card and then will state the correct sum.

Teacher Notes

- Model an example before students begin to play.
- If necessary, prompt students with the sentence frame as they orally supply the numerals for the blanks.
- After all cards have been drawn from the stacks, shuffle each stack separately and then place each set of cards facedown.

Scoring Rubric	
Score	Explanation
3	Students demonstrate an efficient strategy that enables them to solve the problem completely. Students will: • name each numeral correctly. • place the correct number of counters on the mat for each group. • state the correct sum.
2	Students demonstrate a strategy that enables them to solve the problem correctly. The strategy is disorganized or less efficient. Students may: • name the numerals correctly but have difficulty in placing the correct number of counters in each group, while still arriving at the correct sum. • fail to place the counters on the mat but state the correct sum.
1	Students demonstrate a confused strategy that leads to difficulty in solving the problem. Most answers are incorrect, but students demonstrate knowledge of at least one concept. Students may: • be able to name each numeral correctly but unable to place the correct number of counters on the mat and arrive at the correct sum.

Chapter 4

Name

Chapter Pretest

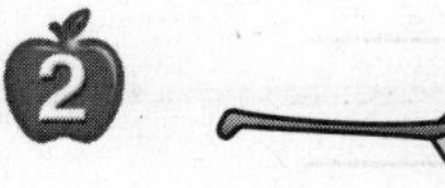

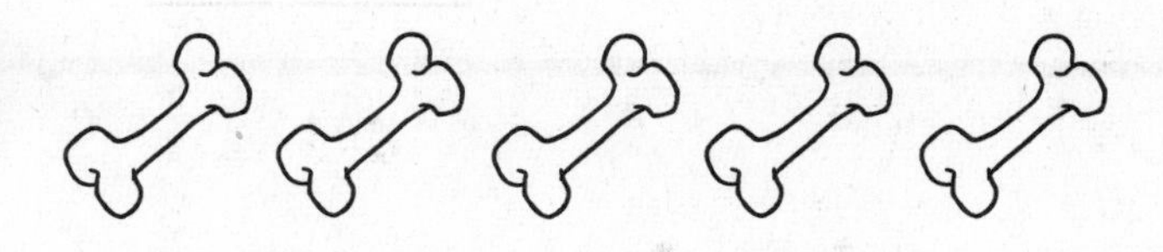

Directions:

1. There are 2 birds in the nest. Then, 1 bird flies away. How many birds are left?
2. There are 4 bugs on a leaf. Then, 2 crawl away. How many bugs are left?
3. Julio has 5 bones. He gives 1 bone to his dog. Draw an X on 1 bone. How many bones are left?
4. There are 6 dogs in the yard. Three dogs go into the house. Draw an X on 3 dogs. How many dogs are left in the yard?

Chapter 4

Name

Chapter Pretest

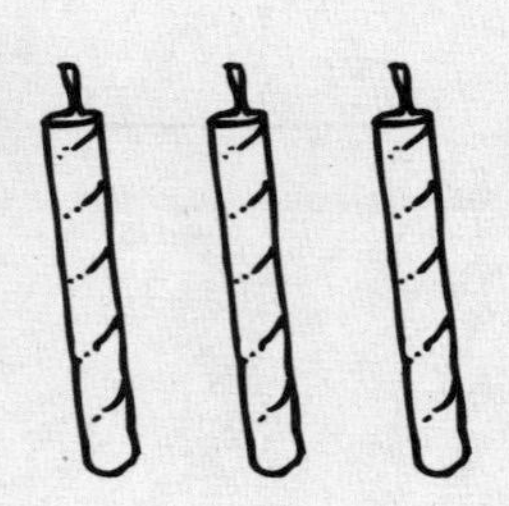

Directions:

5. A store has 7 lamps. A man buys 2 lamps. How many lamps are left?

6. A box has 8 lightbulbs. One lightbulb was taken out of the box. Draw an X on 1 lightbulb. How many lightbulbs are left in the box?

7. There are 9 flashlights on the table. Campers take 5 flashlights. Draw an X on 5 flashlights. How many flashlights are left on the table?

8. There are 3 candles in the kitchen. Dad takes 3 candles out of the kitchen. Draw an X on 3 candles. How many candles are left in the kitchen?

Chapter 4

Chapter Pretest

Scoring Guide and Diagnostic Chart

Students missing Exercise . . .	Have trouble with . . .	Should review . . .
1	Take Away from 1 and 2	Chapter 4, Lesson 1
2	Take Away from 3 and 4	Chapter 4, Lesson 2
3	Take Away from 5	Chapter 4, Lesson 3
4	Take Away from 6	Chapter 4, Lesson 4
5	Take Away from 7	Chapter 4, Lesson 5
6	Take Away from 8	Chapter 4, Lesson 6
7	Take Away from 9	Chapter 4, Lesson 7
8	Take Away from 3 and 4	Chapter 4, Lesson 2

Chapter 4

Name

Chapter Test

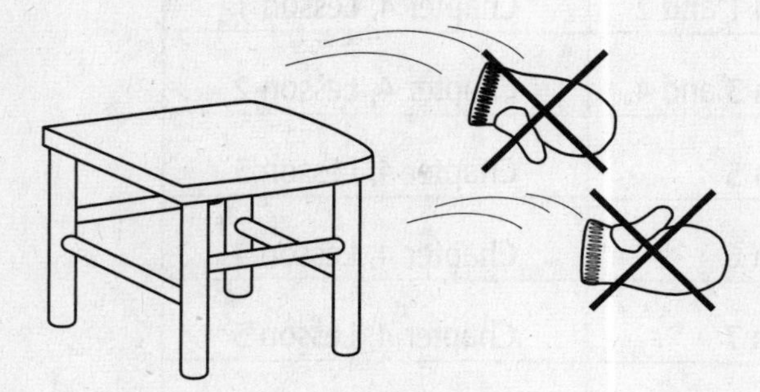

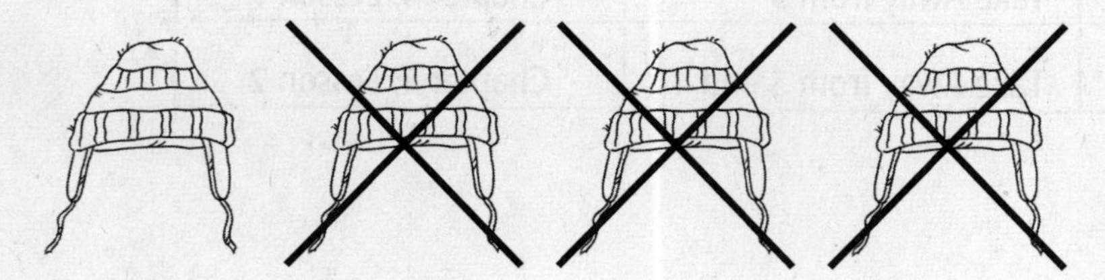

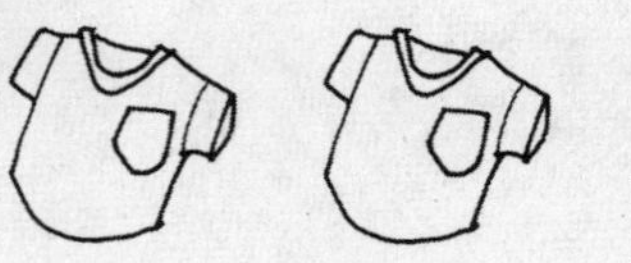

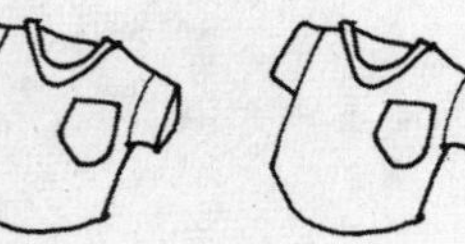

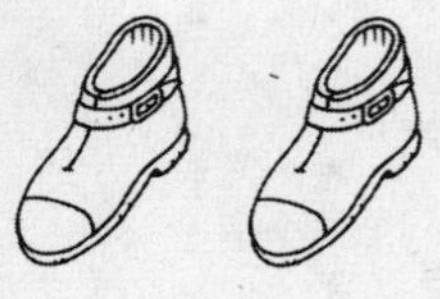

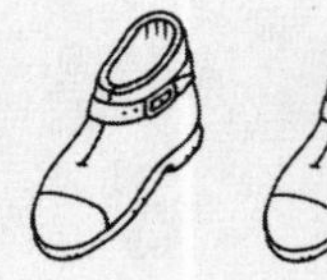

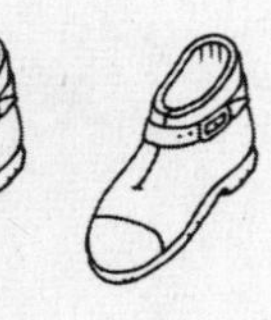

Directions:

1. There are 2 mittens on the table. Then, 2 mittens blow away in the wind. How many mittens are left?
2. There are 4 caps in the closet. The children take 3 caps out of the closet. How many caps are left?
3. There are 5 shirts in the drawer. Isaac takes 2 shirts out of the drawer. Draw Xs on 2 shirts. How many shirts are left in the drawer?
4. There are 6 boots by the door. The dog runs away with 4 of the boots. Draw Xs on 4 boots. How many boots are left by the door?

Chapter 4

Name

Chapter Test

Directions:

5. There are 7 crackers. Lesli eats 4 of the crackers. How many crackers are left?
6. There are 8 cherries in a dish. Jamal takes 6 cherries. Draw an X on 6 cherries. How many cherries are left in the dish?
7. Keisha makes 9 muffins. She gives 3 muffins to her friends. Draw an X on 3 muffins. How many muffins does Keisha have left?
8. A garden has 4 pumpkins. The farmer picks 1 pumpkin. Draw an X on 1 pumpkin. How many pumpkins are left in the garden?

Chapter 4

Chapter 4

Chapter Test

Scoring Guide and Diagnostic Chart

Students missing Exercise . . .	Have trouble with . . .	Should review . . .
1	Take Away from 1 and 2	Chapter 4, Lesson 1
2	Take Away from 3 and 4	Chapter 4, Lesson 2
3	Take Away from 5	Chapter 4, Lesson 3
4	Take Away from 6	Chapter 4, Lesson 4
5	Take Away from 7	Chapter 4, Lesson 5
6	Take Away from 8	Chapter 4, Lesson 6
7	Take Away from 9	Chapter 4, Lesson 7
8	Take Away from 3 and 4	Chapter 4, Lesson 2

Name ______________________

Test Practice

1

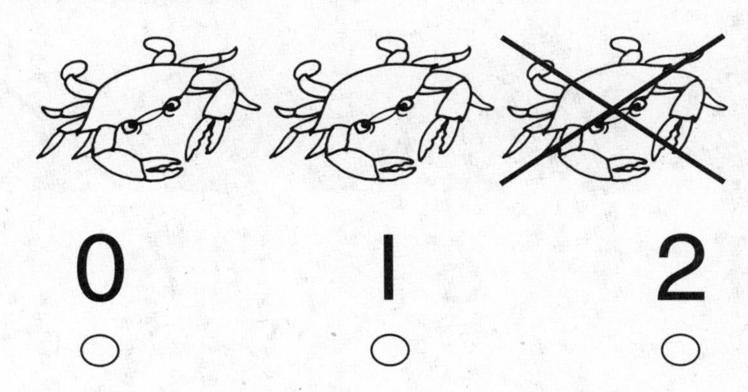

0 ◯ 1 ◯ 2 ◯

2

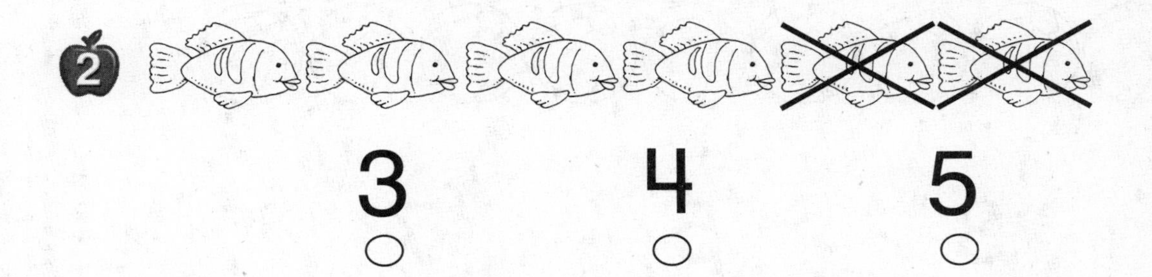

3 ◯ 4 ◯ 5 ◯

3

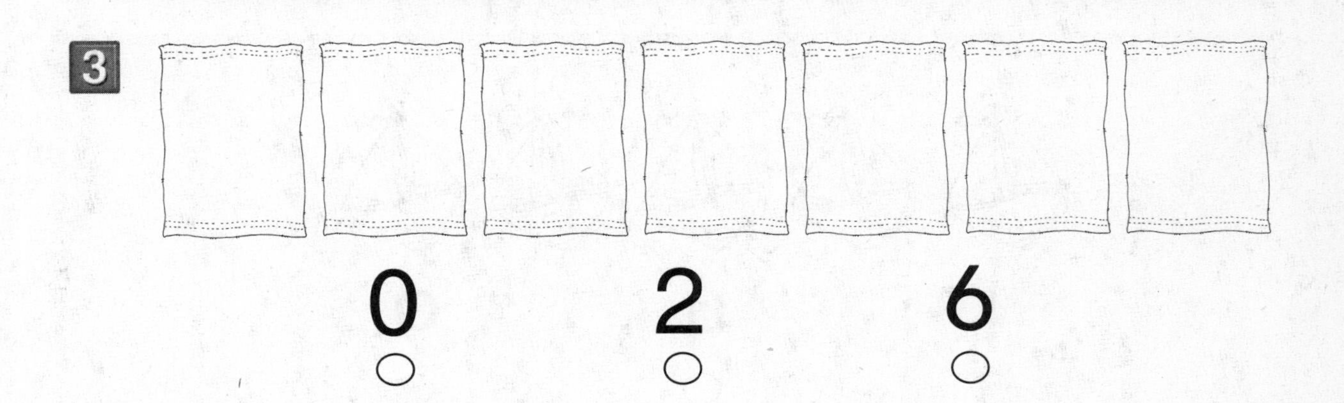

0 ◯ 2 ◯ 6 ◯

Directions:

1. There are 3 crabs on the beach. Then, 1 crab walks away. How many crabs are left on the beach?
2. There are 6 fish swimming near the beach. Then, 2 fish swim away. How many fish are left near the beach?
3. There are 7 towels in the sand. The wind blows 5 towels away. Draw an X an 5 towels. How many towels are left in the sand?

Name ______________________

Test Practice

4 ○ 6 ○ 7 ○

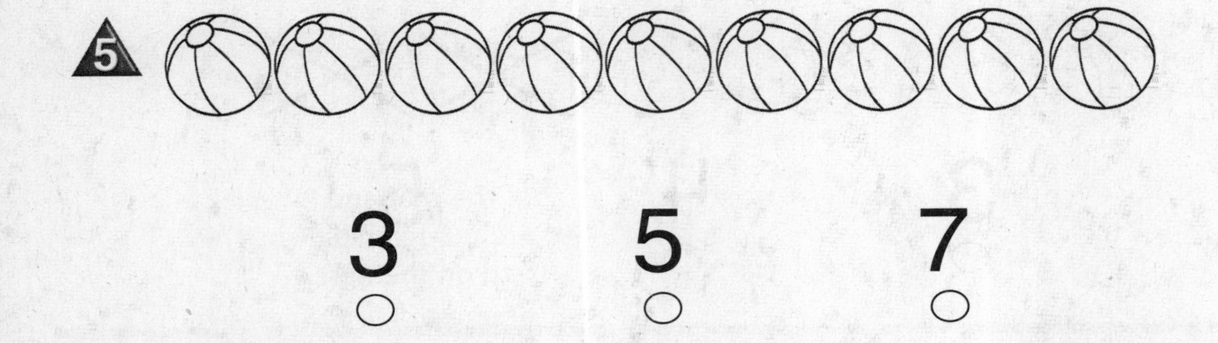

3 ○ 5 ○ 7 ○

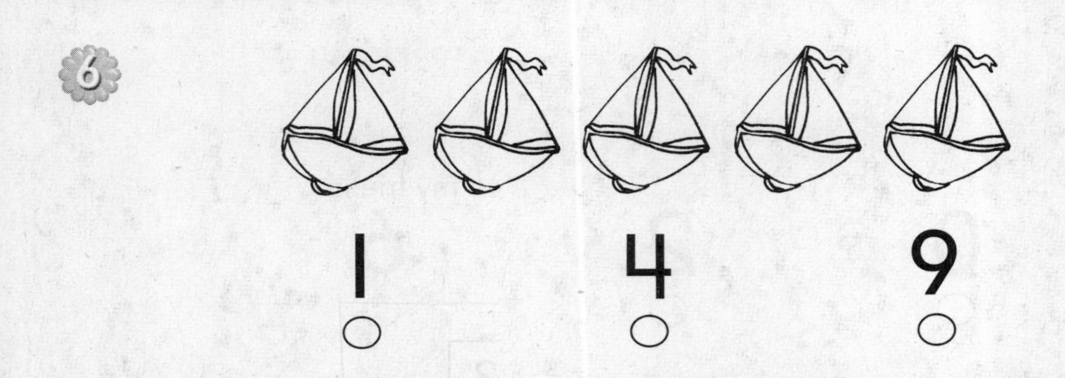

1 ○ 4 ○ 9 ○

Directions:

4. Ahmed has 8 shells in his pail. He gives 2 shells to his sister. How many shells does Ahmed have left in his pail?

5. There are 9 balls on the beach. Then, 4 balls roll into the water. Draw an X on 4 balls. How many balls are left on the beach?

6. Lori has 5 boats in her pail. She puts 4 boats in the water. Draw an X on 4 boats. How many boats does Lori have left in her pail?

Chapter 4

Performance Assessment

STUDENT TASK: Use number cards and buttons to model subtraction sentences.

Teacher Preparation/Instructions:

- Create two stacks of numeral cards. In one stack, include numeral cards 6–9. In the other stack, include numeral cards 0–5.
- Place ten buttons of similar size in a cup.
- Provide a mat.
- Ask students to pretend they are making cookies for their friends. Encourage students to pretend each button is a cookie.

Lead students through the following steps:

- The student draws a numeral from the 6–9 stack and reads the numeral aloud.
- The student places the card on the left of the mat and places the correct number of buttons below the card.
- The student draws a numeral card from the 0–5 stack. This will be the number of cookies to take away. The student reads the numeral aloud.
- The student places the card on the right of the mat and takes away the correct number of buttons to match the numeral, placing the buttons taken away below the numeral card on the right.
- The student uses the following sentence frame to tell how many are left. Have the student echo the sentence frames while orally filling in the correct numbers.

I made ______ cookies. I gave ______ cookies to my friends. Now, I have ______ cookies left.

For example:

I made seven cookies. I gave three cookies to my friends. Now, I have four cookies left.

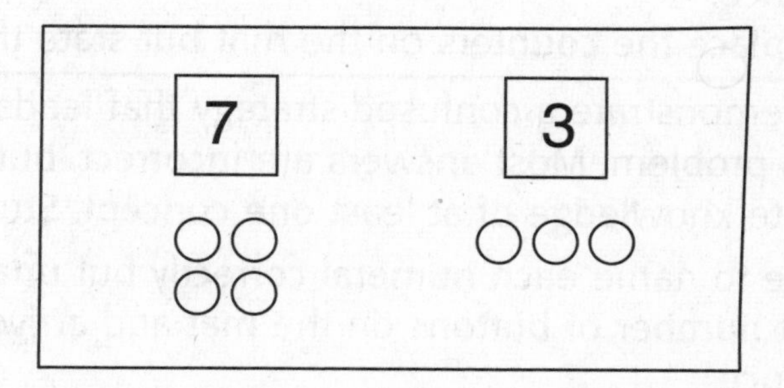

Performance Assessment Teacher's Notes

Target Skills

- Subtract from 1 to 9.

Task Description

Students will choose a numeral card from one card stack and a numeral card from another stack. Then, students will read each numeral aloud and place each card on a mat with the appropriate number of buttons. Finally, students will use a sentence frame to tell how many are left.

Teacher Notes

- Model an example before students begin to play.
- After all cards have been drawn from the stack, shuffle the stack and place the cards facedown to continue play.

Scoring Rubric	
Score	**Explanation**
3	Students demonstrate an efficient strategy that enables them to solve the problem completely. Students will: • name each numeral correctly. • place the correct number of buttons on the mat for each group. • state the correct difference.
2	Students demonstrate a strategy that enables them to solve the problem correctly. The strategy is disorganized or less efficient. Students may: • name the numerals correctly but have difficulty in placing the correct number of buttons in each group, while still arriving at the correct difference. • fail to place the counters on the mat but state the correct difference.
1	Students demonstrate a confused strategy that leads to difficulty in solving the problem. Most answers are incorrect, but students demonstrate knowledge of at least one concept. Students may: • be able to name each numeral correctly but unable to place the correct number of buttons on the mat and arrive at the correct difference.

Name

Section Test (Chapters 1–4)

 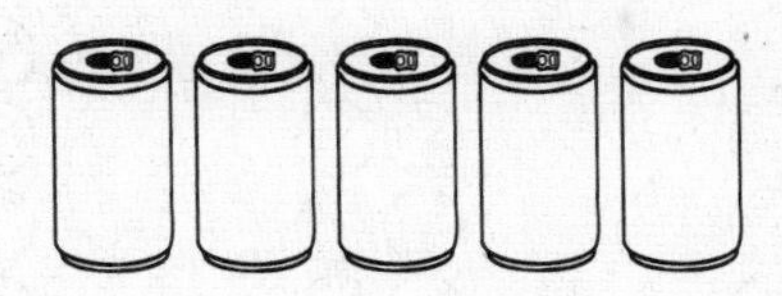 

○ ○ ○

   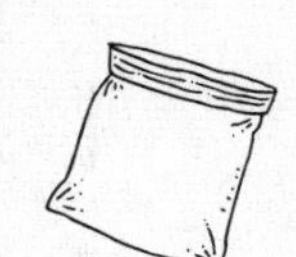

3 4 1

○ ○ ○

○ ○ ○

Name ______________________

Section Test (Chapters 1–4)

  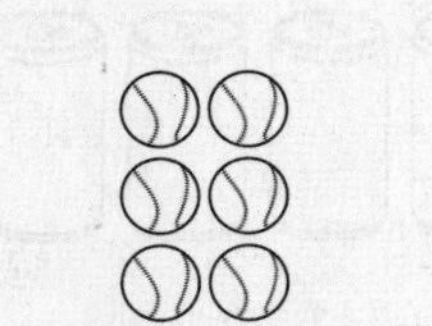 

4 5 ____ 7

6 ○ 1 ○ 3 ○

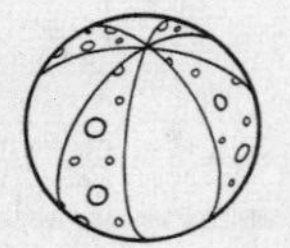 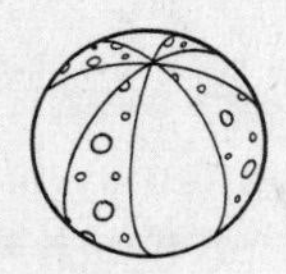 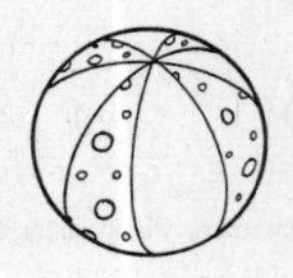 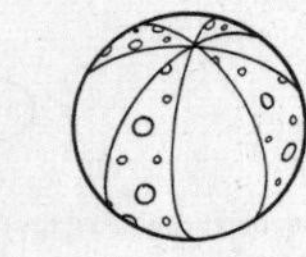

3 ○ 2 ○ 4 ○

3 ○ 1 ○ 6 ○

2 ○ 7 ○ 4 ○

Section Test (Chapters 1–4)

Scoring Guide and Diagnostic Chart

Students missing Exercise...	Have trouble with...	Should review...
1	Count Objects 0 to 5	Chapter 1, Lesson 1
2	Numbers 4 and 5	Chapter 1, Lesson 7
3	First, Next, Last	Chapter 2, Lesson 2
4	More Number Patterns	Chapter 2, Lesson 8
5	Sums of 3 and 4	Chapter 3, Lesson 2
6	Take Away from 5	Chapter 4, Lesson 3
7	Take Away from 7	Chapter 4, Lesson 5

Teacher Directions

Read the following directions to students before they begin. Then, read each question followed by a pause to allow students time to work and choose an answer.

- **Write your name at the top of the page.**
- **I am going to read each question to you. Listen carefully before you choose an answer.**

1. Count the objects. Which is a group of four?
2. How many plastic bags are there?
3. Find the turkey. Which animal comes next in line?

- **Turn the page over.**

4. Look for a pattern. Which number is missing?
5. Derek had one beach ball. Tony had three beach balls. How many beach balls did Derek and Tony have in all?
6. There were five muffins in the box. Marla and her sisters ate four muffins. How many muffins are left in the box?
7. Seven tacos were on the dish. Ted and his friends ate five tacos. How many tacos are left on the dish?

Name

Section Pretest (Chapters 5–7)

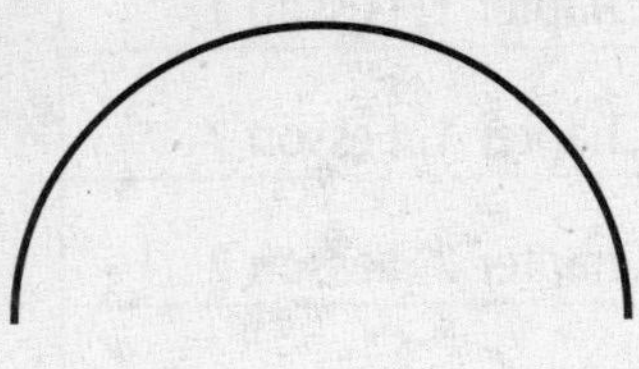 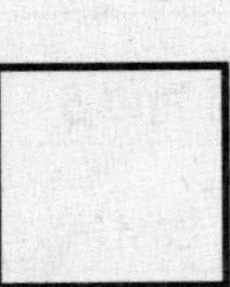 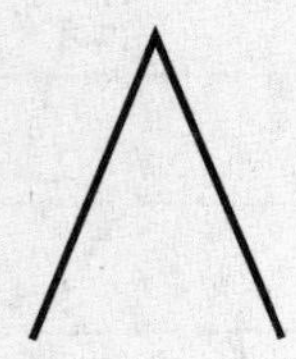

4 0 3

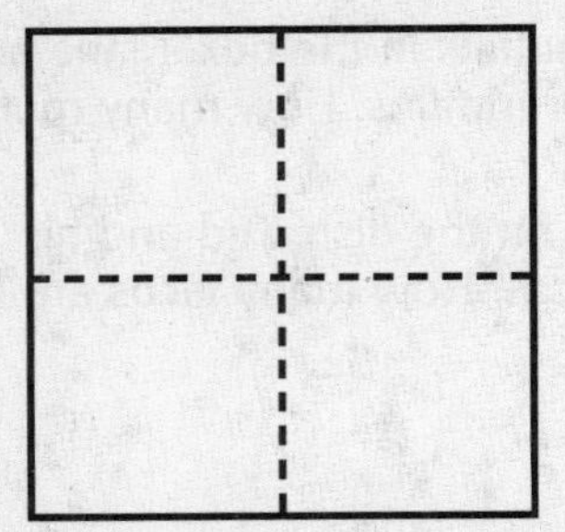

 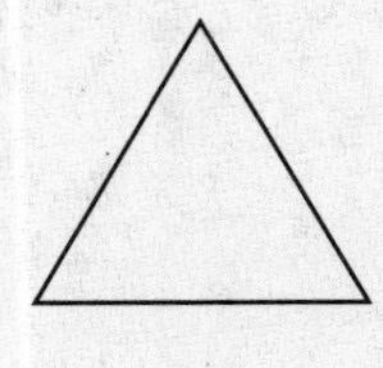 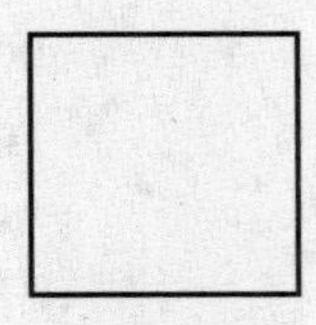

Name

Section Pretest (Chapters 5–7)

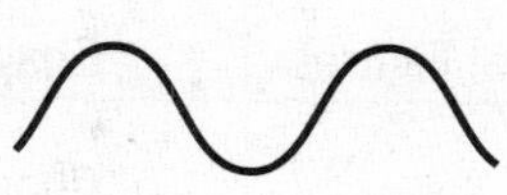

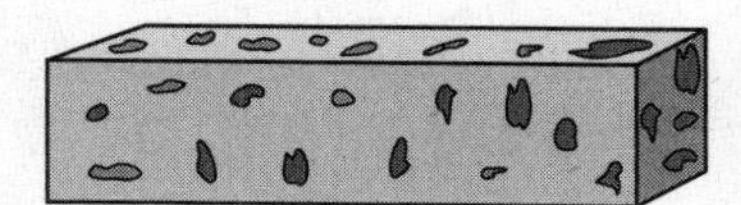

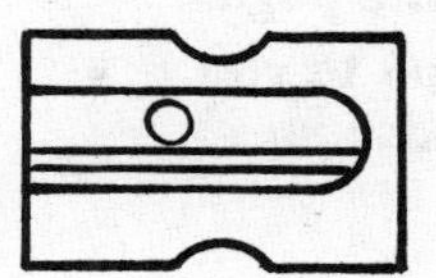

Section Pretest

Section Pretest (Chapters 5–7)
Scoring Guide and Diagnostic Chart

Students missing Exercise...	Have trouble with...	Should review...
1	Open or Closed Figures	Chapter 5, Lesson 1
2	Rectangles	Chapter 5, Lesson 5
3	Create Two-Dimensional Figures	Chapter 5, Lesson 7
4	Curved or Straight	Chapter 5, Lesson 2
5	Roll and Stack	Chapter 6, Lesson 2
6	Cylinders	Chapter 6, Lesson 4
7	Top, Middle, or Bottom	Chapter 7, Lesson 3

Teacher Directions
Read the following directions to students before they begin. Then, read each question followed by a pause to allow students time to work and choose an answer.

- **Write your name at the top of the page.**
- **I am going to read each question to you. Listen carefully before you choose an answer.**

1. Which is a closed figure?
2. How many sides are in the figure?
3. Which figure is used to make the square?

- **Turn the page over.**

4. Which is a curved line?
5. Which object can be rolled?
6. Which object is a cylinder?
7. Which picture shows the bug in the middle?

Chapter 5

Name

Chapter Pretest

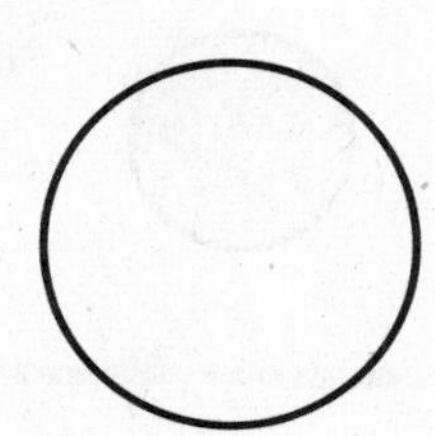

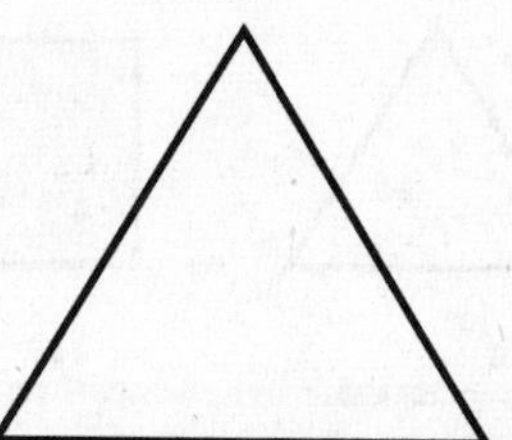

2

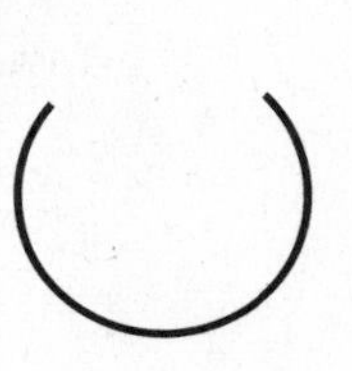
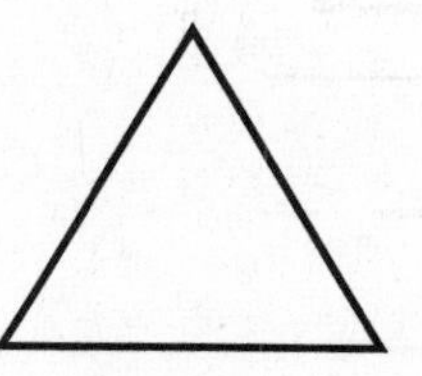

3

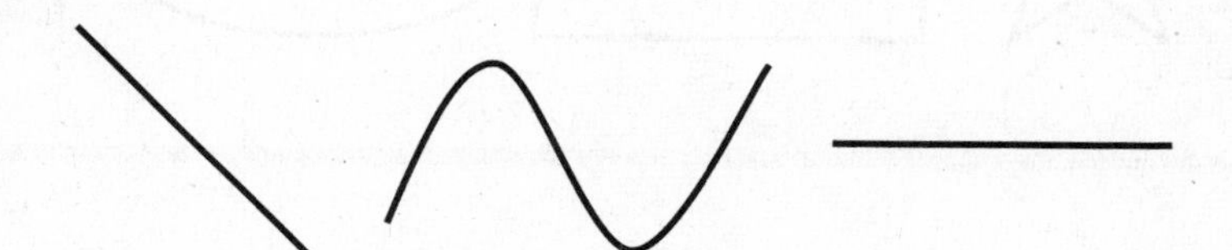

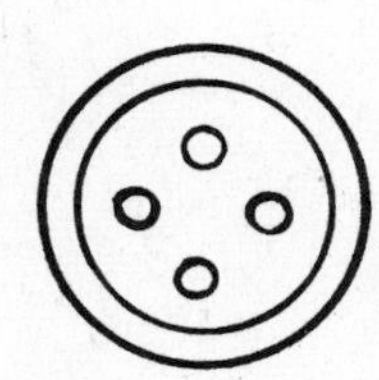

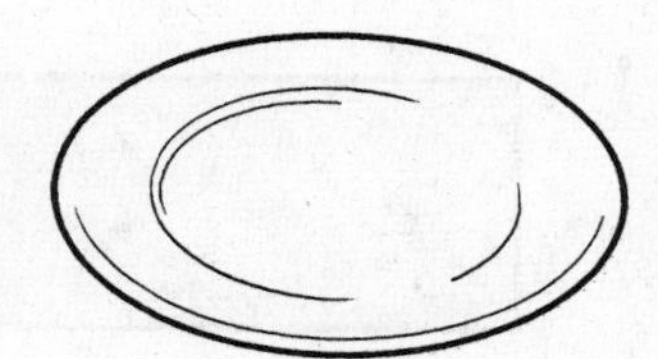
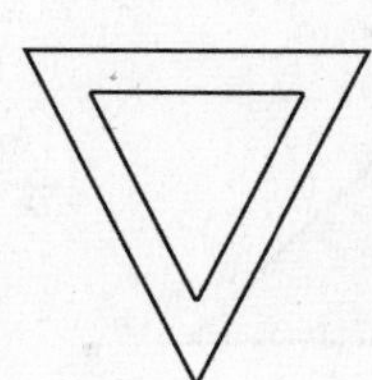

Directions:

1. Draw an X on the open figure.
2. Circle the closed figure.
3. Circle the curved line.
4. Draw an X on the circle.

Chapter 5

Name

Chapter Pretest

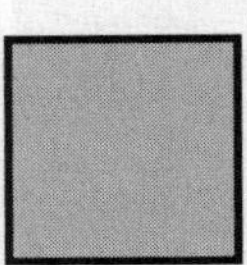
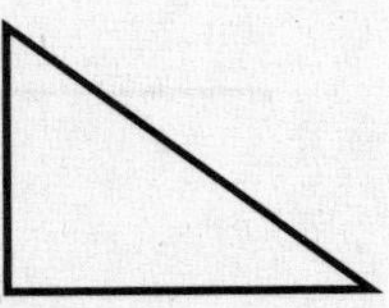

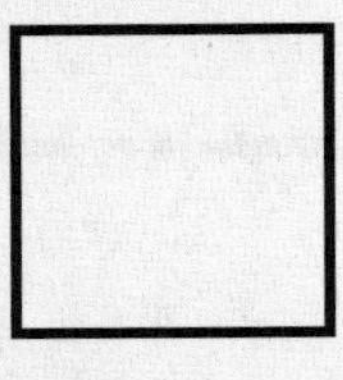

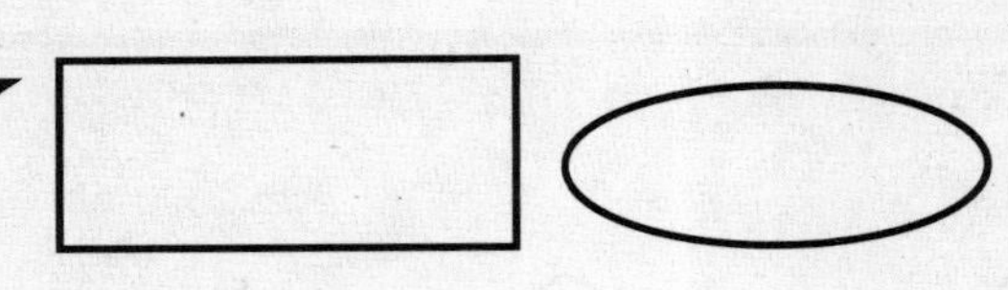

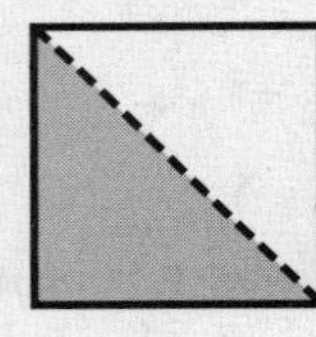
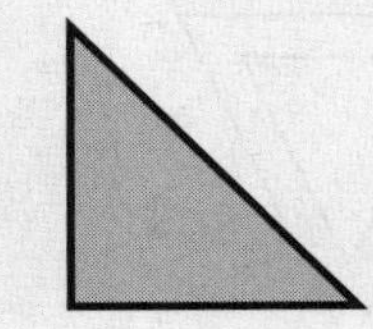
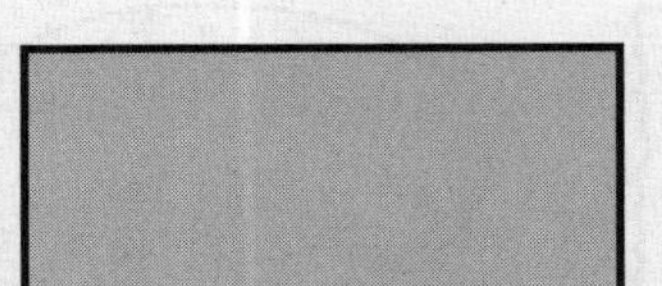

Directions:

5. Draw an X on the figures with three corners.
6. Write the number of sides for each figure.
7. Draw an X on the square.
8. Draw an X on the figure that is used to make the square.

Chapter Pretest

Scoring Guide and Diagnostic Chart

Students missing Exercise . . .	Have trouble with . . .	Should review . . .
1	Open or Closed Figures	Chapter 5, Lesson 1
2	Open or Closed Figures	Chapter 5, Lesson 1
3	Curved or Straight	Chapter 5, Lesson 2
4	Circles	Chapter 5, Lesson 3
5	Triangles	Chapter 5, Lesson 4
6	Rectangles	Chapter 5, Lesson 5
7	Squares	Chapter 5, Lesson 6
8	Create Two-Dimensional Figures	Chapter 5, Lesson 7

Chapter 5

Name

Chapter Test

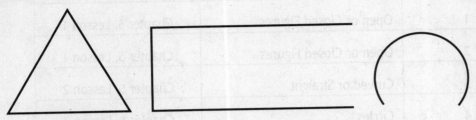

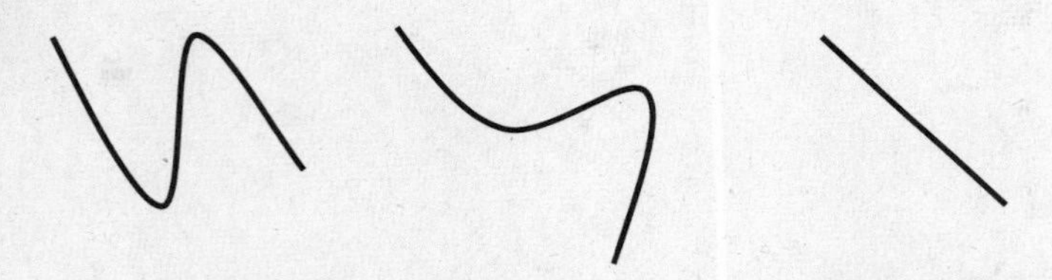

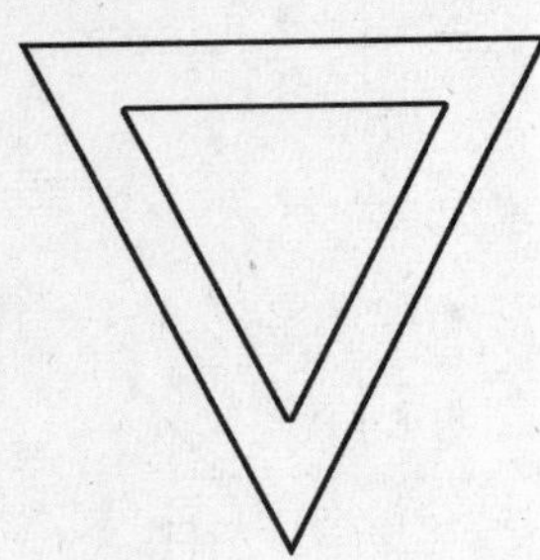

Directions:

1. Draw an X on the closed figure.
2. Draw an open figure.
3. Circle the straight line.
4. Draw an X on the two circles.

Name ______________________

Chapter Test

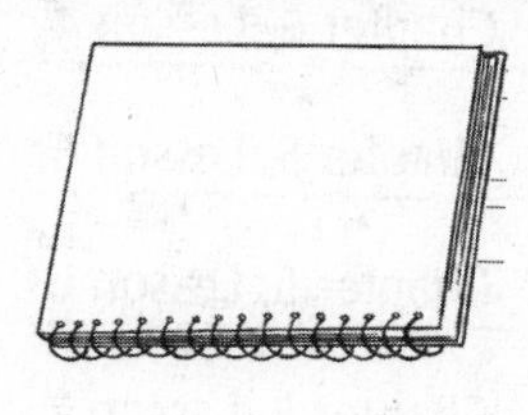

______

______

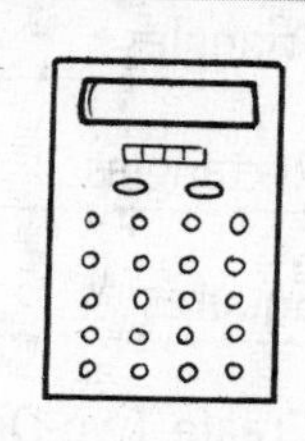

______

______

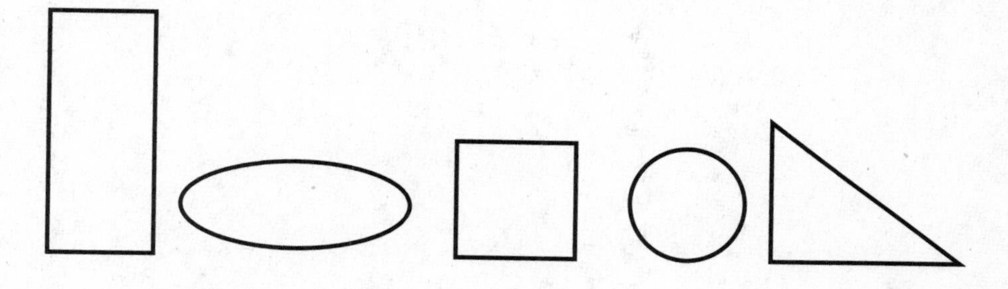

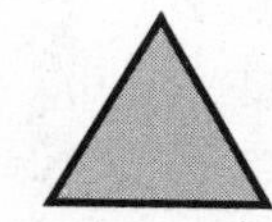

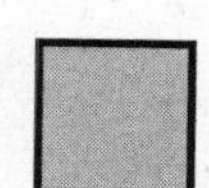

Directions:

5. Draw an X on the figures with three corners.
6. Write the number of sides for each figure.
7. Draw an X on the square.
8. Draw an X on the figure that is used to make the rectangle.

Chapter 5

Chapter Test

Scoring Guide and Diagnostic Chart

Students missing Exercise . . .	Have trouble with . . .	Should review . . .
1	Open or Closed Figures	Chapter 5, Lesson 1
2	Open or Closed Figures	Chapter 5, Lesson 1
3	Curved or Straight	Chapter 5, Lesson 2
4	Circles	Chapter 5, Lesson 3
5	Triangles	Chapter 5, Lesson 4
6	Rectangles	Chapter 5, Lesson 5
7	Squares	Chapter 5, Lesson 6
8	Create Two-Dimensional Figures	Chapter 5, Lesson 7

Name

Test Practice

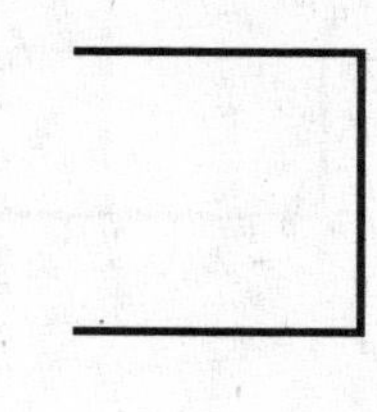 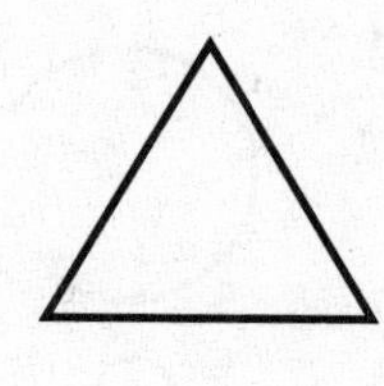 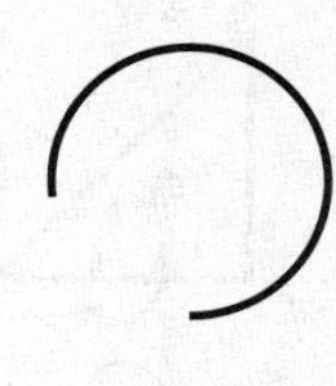

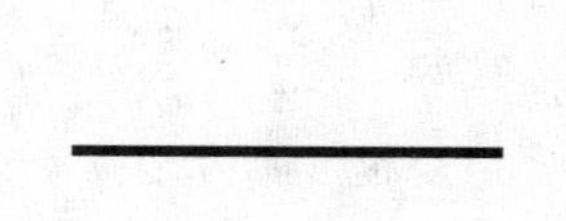  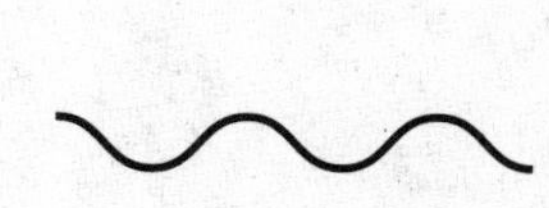

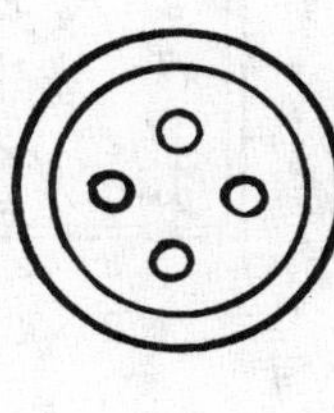 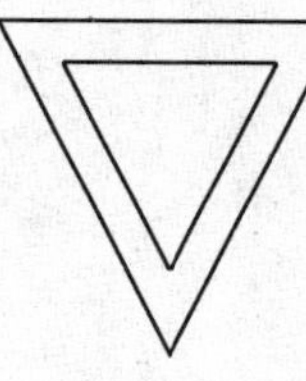 

 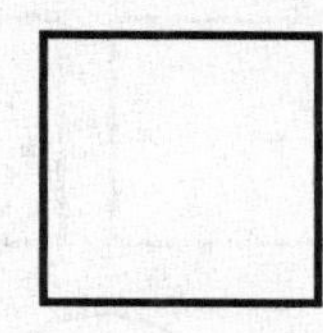 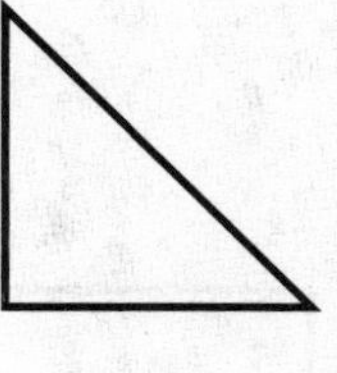

Directions:

1. Which is a closed figure?
2. Which is a curved line?
3. Which object is a circle?
4. Which figure has three corners?

Name

Test Practice

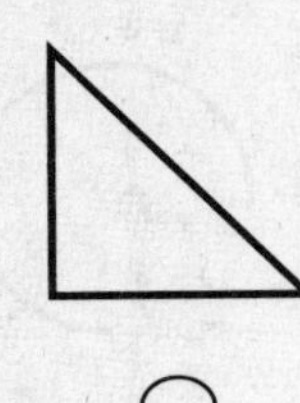 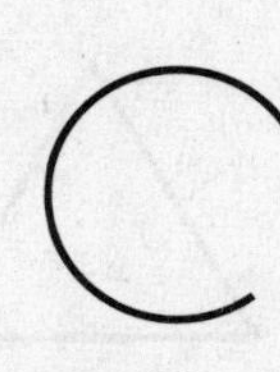 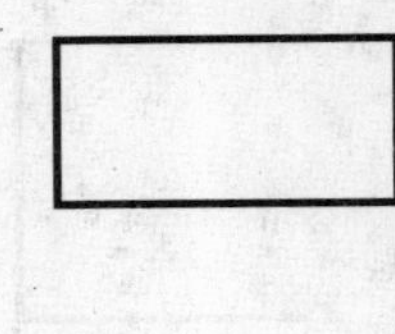

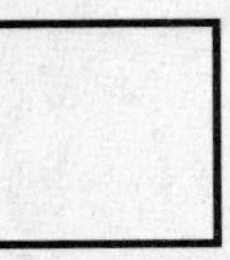

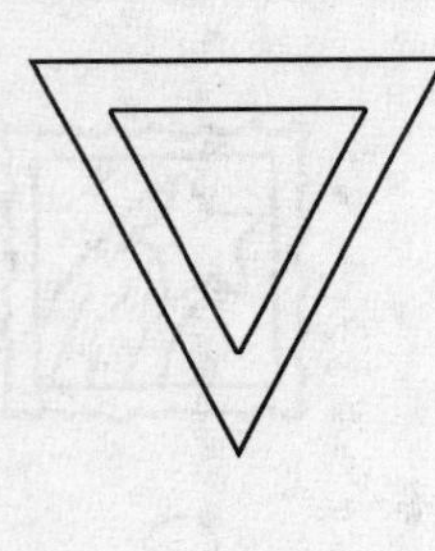 

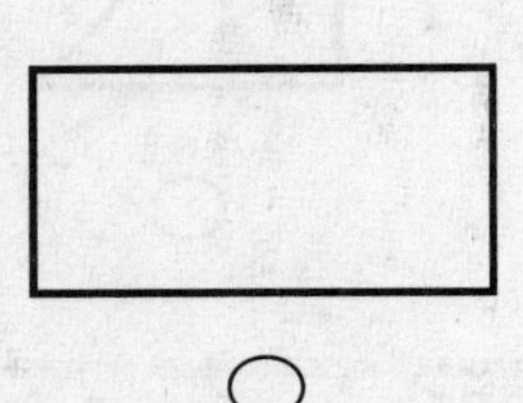 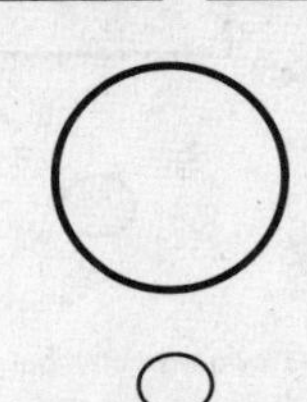 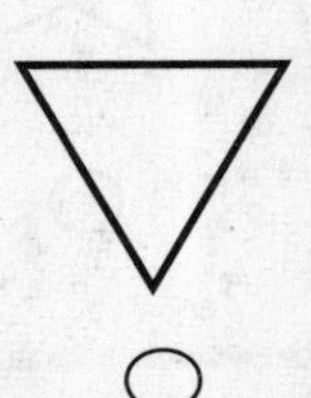

Directions:

5. Which is an open figure?
6. How many sides does the figure have?
7. Which object has four corners?
8. Which figure would the two squares make?

Chapter 5

Performance Assessment

STUDENT TASK: Answer riddles to identify two-dimensional figures.

Teacher Preparation/Instructions:

- For each student provide mats and the following shapes: square, rectangle, circle, triangle.
- Tell students they will play a game. Explain that they should answer each riddle by placing the correct shape on the mat and naming the figure.

Lead students through the following steps:

- Read aloud a riddle.
- The student places the correct shape on the mat to answer the riddle.
- The student names the figure by using one of the sentence frames:

I am a ______.
We are a ______ and a ______.

Riddles:

1. I am a circle. Which figure am I?
2. I am a square. Which figure am I?
3. I am a triangle. Which figure am I?
4. I am a rectangle. Which figure am I?
5. I have three corners. What am I? (a triangle)
6. We have four sides. What are we? (a square and a rectangle)
7. I have no sides. Which figure am I? (a circle)
8. We have four corners. What are we? (a square and a rectangle)
9. I have three sides. What am I? (a triangle)
10. We are closed figures. What are we? (all figures)
11. I have the same shape as that of a wheel. What am I? (a circle)
12. You can use us to make the shapes of a train car. What are we? (a square or a rectangle and a circle)

Chapter 5

Performance Assessment Teacher's Notes

Target Skill

- Identify circles, triangles, rectangles, and squares.
- Identify attributes of circles, triangles, rectangles, and squares.
- Identify closed figures.

Task Description

Students will answer riddles to identify two-dimensional figures.

Teacher Notes

Model an example before students begin to play. For the shapes you can use pattern blocks, attribute buttons, attribute links, or other objects in the classroom.

Scoring Rubric	
Score	Explanation
3	Students demonstrate an efficient strategy that enables them to solve the problem completely. Students will: • name each figure correctly. • place the correct shape on the mat.
2	Students demonstrate a strategy that enables them to solve the problem correctly. The strategy is disorganized or less efficient. Students may: • name the correct figure but be unable to locate the correct shape. • incorrectly name the figure but be able to locate the correct shape.
1	Students demonstrate a confused strategy that leads to difficulty in solving the problem. Most answers are incorrect, but students demonstrate knowledge of at least one concept. Students may: • be able to name or locate two, or fewer than two, figures in response to riddles.

Chapter 6

Name

Chapter Pretest

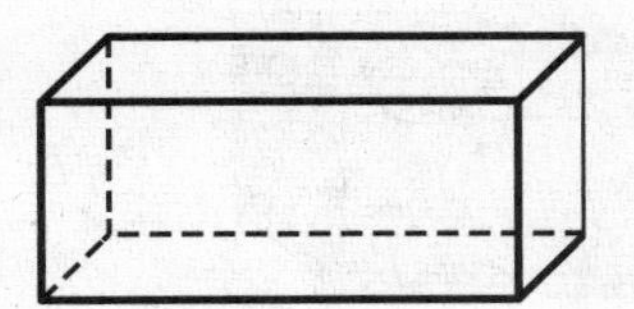

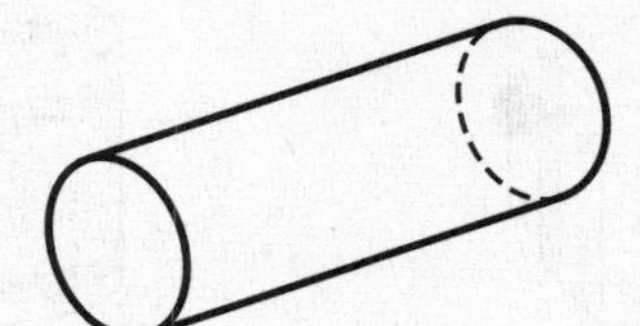

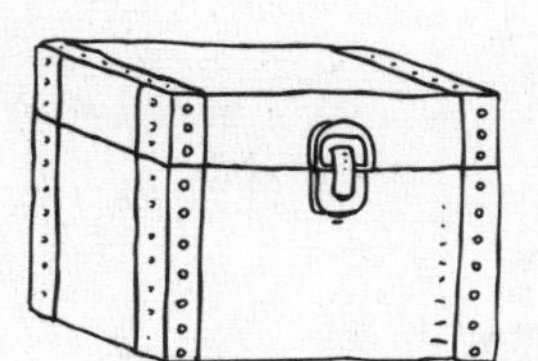

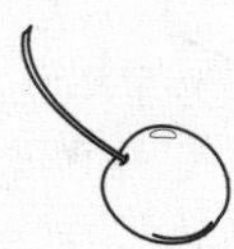

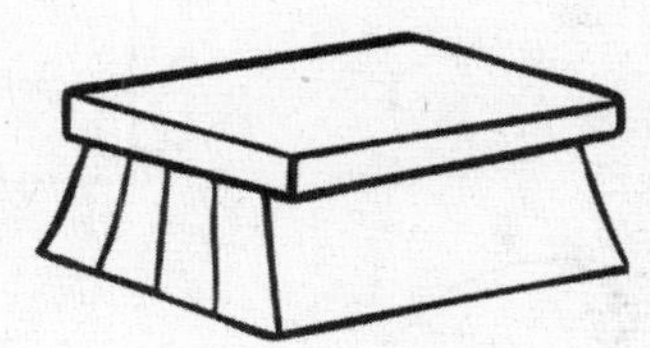

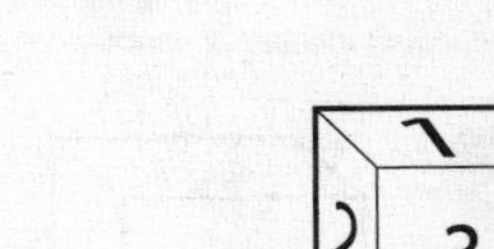

Directions:

1. Draw an X on the object that has a circle as one of its faces.
2. Draw an X on the object that can be rolled.
3. Draw an X on the object that can be stacked.
4. Draw an X on the sphere.

Name ______________________

Chapter Pretest

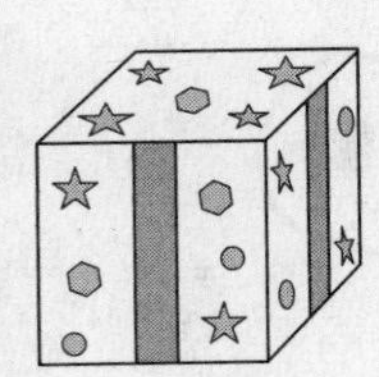

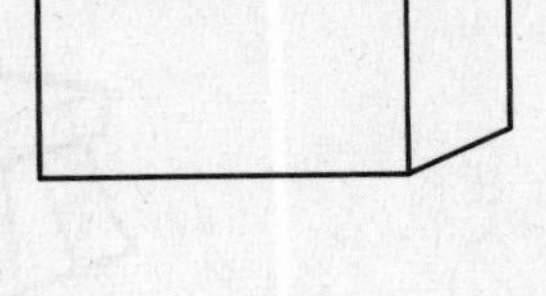

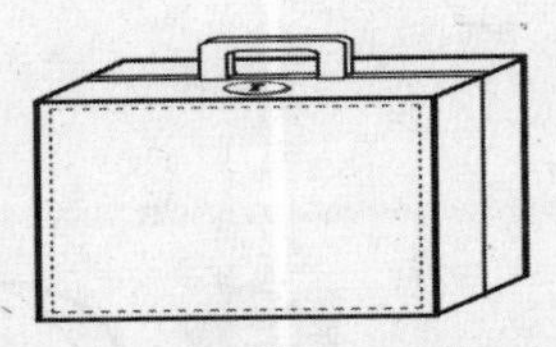

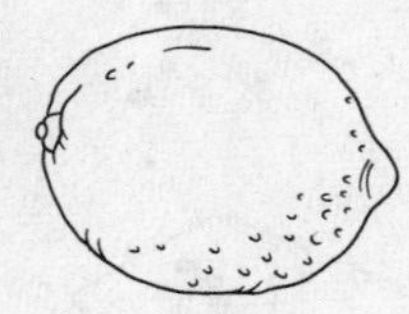
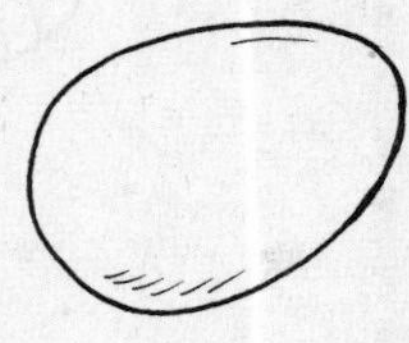
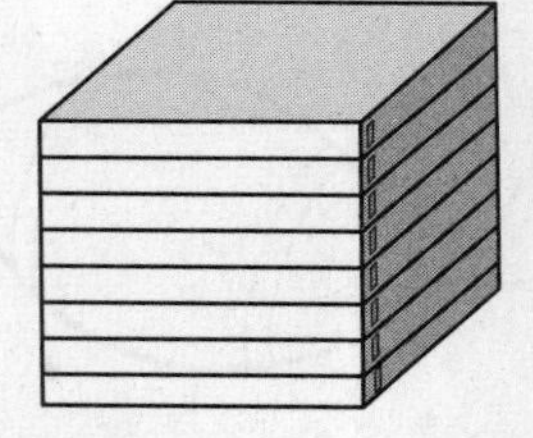

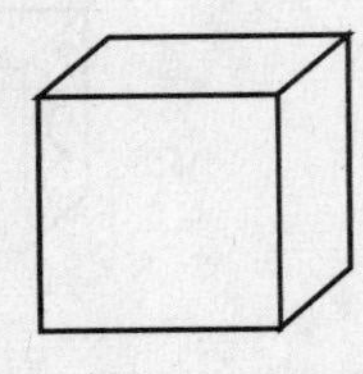
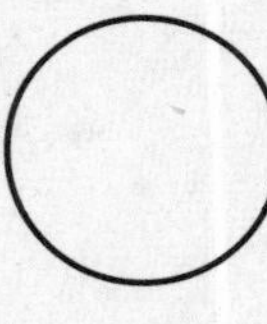

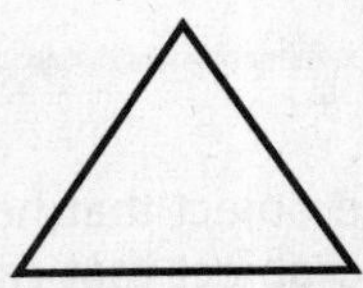

Directions:

5. Draw an X on the cylinder.
6. Connect the rectangular prisms with a line.
7. Draw an X on the cube.
8. Draw an X on the shape that is a face of the cube.

Chapter 6

Chapter Pretest

Scoring Guide and Diagnostic Chart

Students missing Exercise . . .	Have trouble with . . .	Should review . . .
1	Introduce Three-Dimensional Figures	Chapter 6, Lesson 1
2	Roll and Stack	Chapter 6, Lesson 2
3	Roll and Stack	Chapter 6, Lesson 2
4	Spheres	Chapter 6, Lesson 3
5	Cylinders	Chapter 6, Lesson 4
6	Rectangular Prisms	Chapter 6, Lesson 5
7	Cubes	Chapter 6, Lesson 6
8	Create Three-Dimensional Figures	Chapter 6, Lesson 7

Chapter 6

Name ______________________

Chapter Test

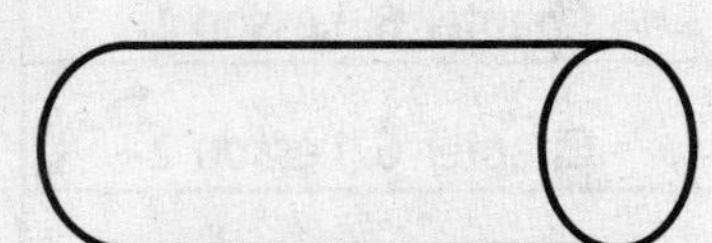
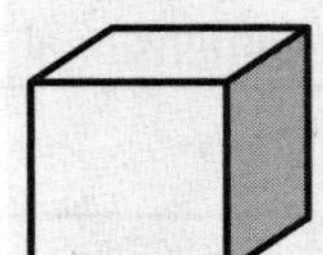

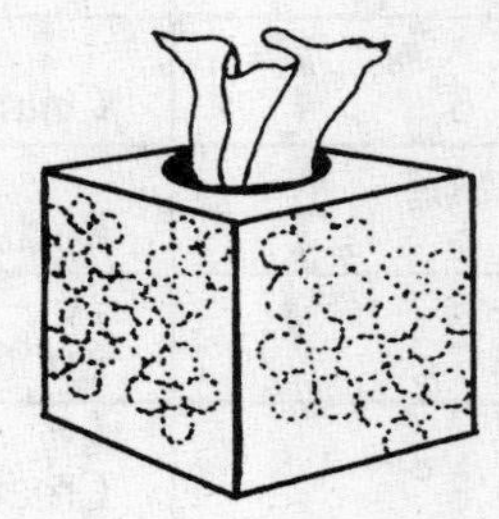

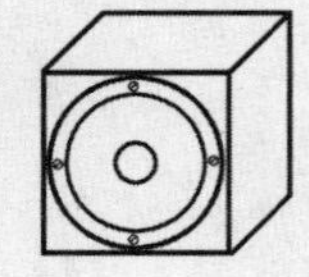

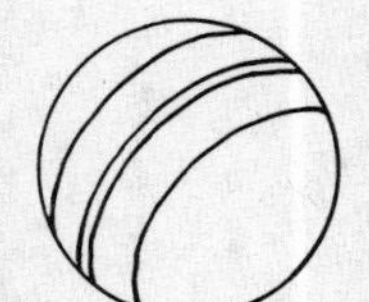

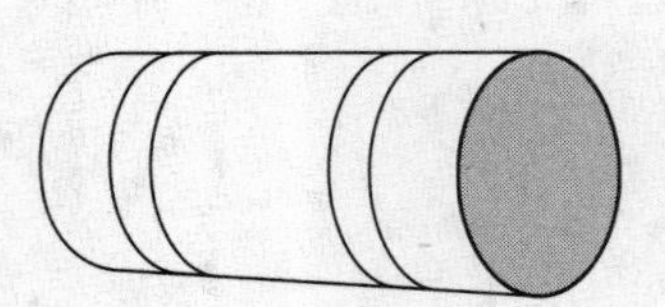
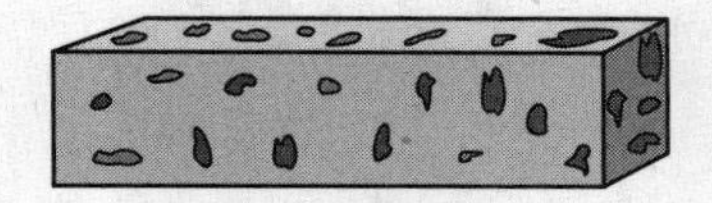

Directions:

1. Draw an X on the object that has a circle as one of its faces.
2. Draw an X on the object that can be rolled.
3. Draw an X on the object that can be stacked.
4. Draw an X on the sphere.

Name

Chapter Test

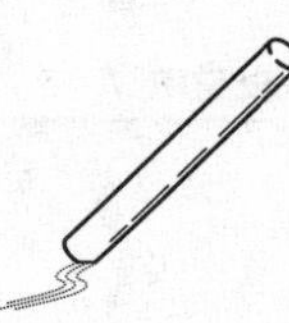

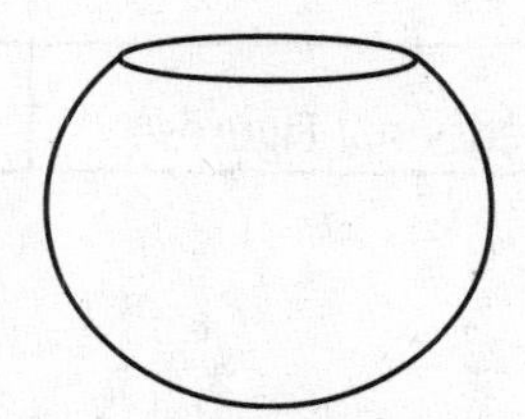

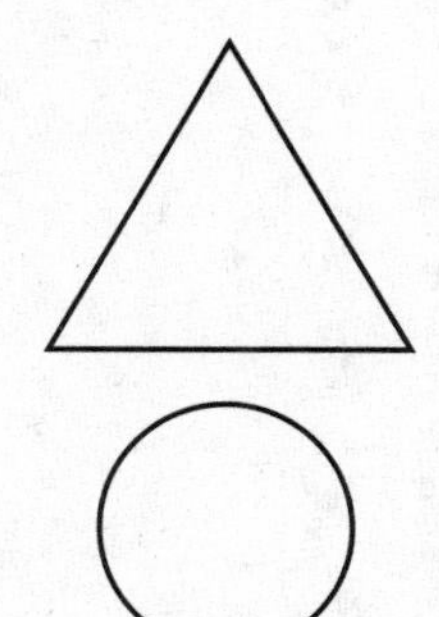

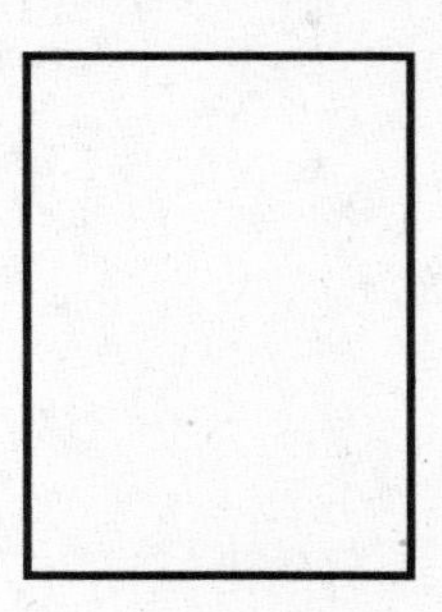

Directions:

5. Draw an X on the cylinder.
6. Connect the rectangular prisms with a line.
7. Draw an X on the cube.
8. Draw an X on the shape that is a face of the box.

Chapter 6

Chapter Test

Scoring Guide and Diagnostic Chart

Students missing Exercise . . .	Have trouble with . . .	Should review . . .
1	Introduce Three-Dimensional Figures	Chapter 6, Lesson 1
2	Roll and Stack	Chapter 6, Lesson 2
3	Roll and Stack	Chapter 6, Lesson 2
4	Spheres	Chapter 6, Lesson 3
5	Cylinders	Chapter 6, Lesson 4
6	Rectangular Prisms	Chapter 6, Lesson 5
7	Cubes	Chapter 6, Lesson 6
8	Create Three-Dimensional Figures	Chapter 6, Lesson 7

Name

Test Practice

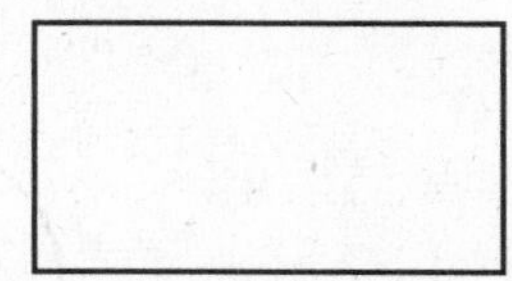

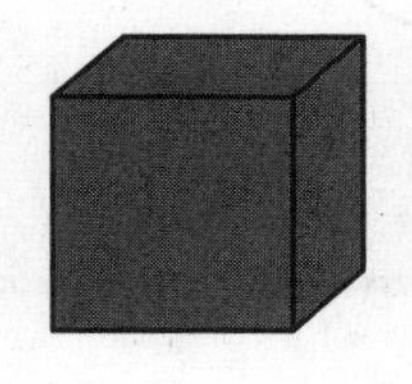 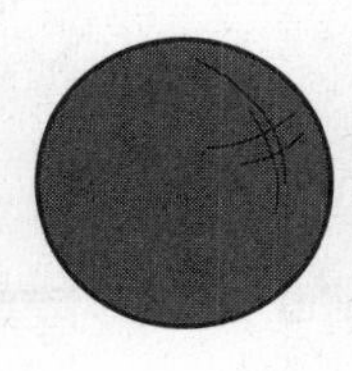 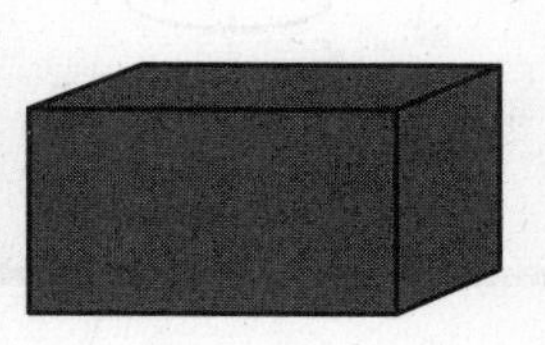

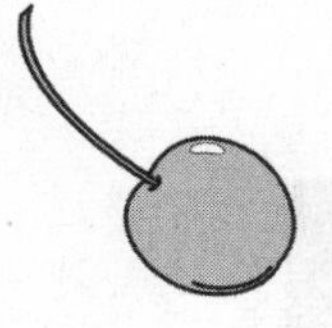  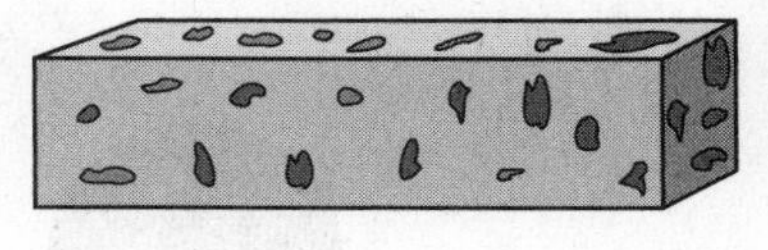

 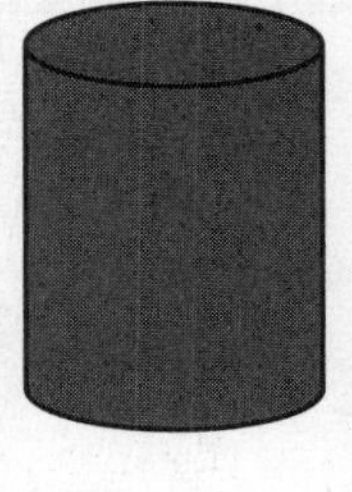 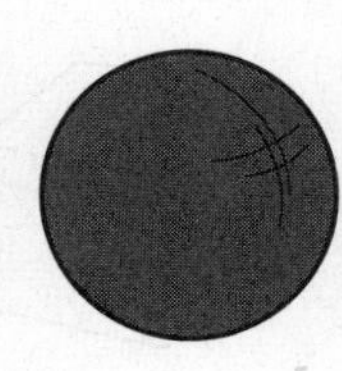

Directions:

1. Look at the rectangle. Which figure has a rectangle as one of its faces?
2. Look at the objects. Which object can be rolled?
3. Look at the figures. Which is a cylinder?

Name

Test Practice

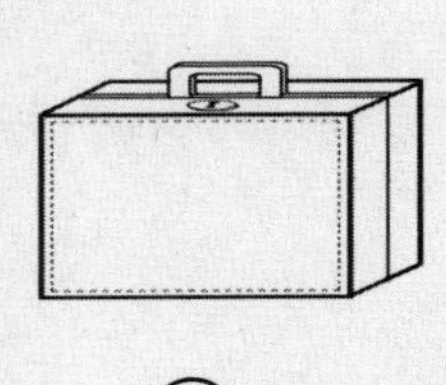

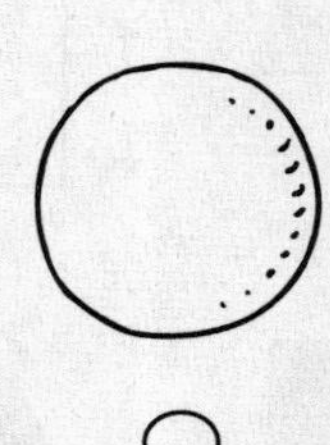

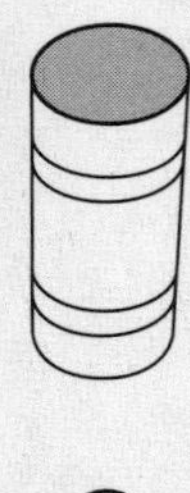

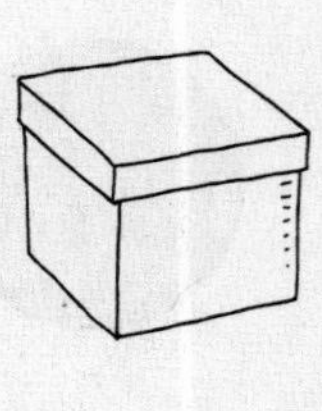

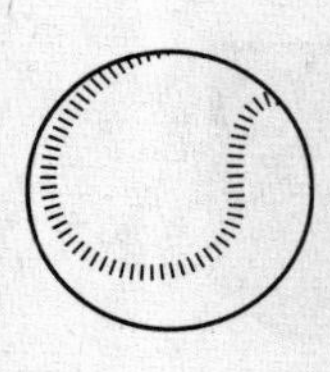

Directions:

4. Look at the figures. Which a rectangular prism?
5. Look at the square. Which solid has a square as one of its faces?
6. Look at the objects. Which is a sphere?

Chapter 6 Performance Assessment

STUDENT'S TASK: Students will take illustrations of three-dimensional figures from a stack, name each figure, and match the illustration to the correct figure. Additionally, students will tell whether the matched item can be rolled or stacked.

TEACHER PREPARATION/INSTRUCTIONS

Place the following items on a table: an empty paper towel core (on its side), a rectangular game box, a ball, and a geometric cube.

- Paste an illustration of each of the following to an index card: cylinder, sphere, rectangular prism, and cube.
- Place the index cards facedown in a stack.
- Tell students that they will play a matching game. Explain that they will take a figure card, name the figure, match it to an item on a table, and answer a question about it.

ONE WAY:

1. Take the top card and turn it over.
2. Name the figure.
3. Place the card on the table in front of an object that has the same shape.
4. Ask: "Can this object be rolled?"
5. Ask: "Can this object be stacked?"

ANOTHER WAY:

Point to objects on the table and ask the following questions:

- Which looks like a sphere?
- Which looks like a rectangular prism?
- Which looks like a cube?
- Which looks like a cylinder?

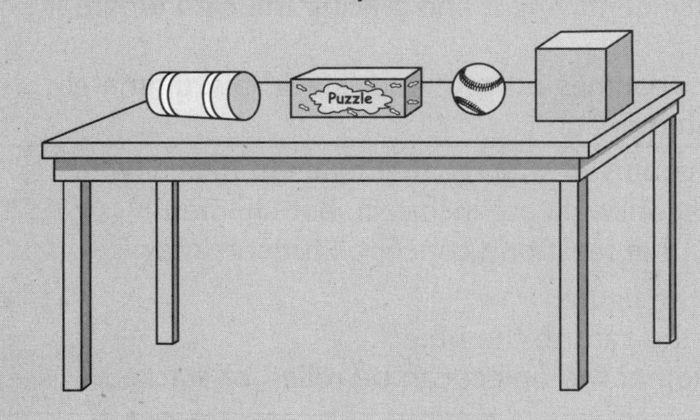

Chapter 6

Performance Assessment Teacher's Notes

Target Skills

- Identify three-dimensional objects—cube, cylinder, rectangular prism, and sphere.
- Determine whether specific three-dimensional objects can be rolled or stacked.

Task Description

Students will take illustrations of three-dimensional figures from a stack, name each figure, and then match the illustration to the correct figure. Additionally, students will tell whether the matched item can be rolled or stacked.

Teacher Notes

- Model an example before students begin to play.
- After all four cards have been pulled from the stack, shuffle the cards and place them facedown for continued play.

Scoring Rubric	
Score	Explanation
3	Students demonstrate an efficient strategy that enables them to solve the problem completely. Students will: • correctly name the figure. • correctly match the figure to the object. • correctly tell whether the figure can be rolled or stacked.
2	Students demonstrate a strategy that enables them to solve the problem correctly. The strategy is disorganized or less efficient. Students may: • move the card from object to object and initially incorrectly name the figure before correctly identifying it and placing the card where it belongs. • initially confuse the meanings of "roll" and "stack" but ultimately make the correct determination.
1	Students demonstrate a confused strategy that leads to difficulty in solving the problem. Most answers are incorrect, but children demonstrate knowledge of at least one concept. Students may: • be unable to name the figure. • be unable to match the card to the object. • be unable to tell whether the object can be rolled or stacked.

Chapter 7

Name

Chapter Pretest

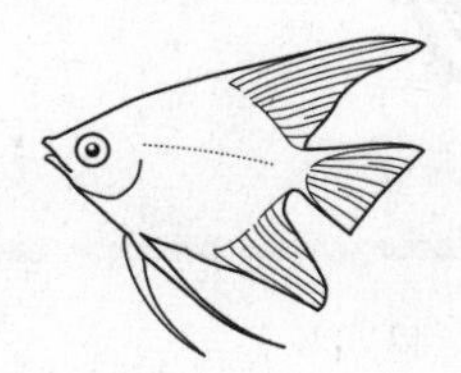

Directions:

1. Draw a circle around the animal after the turtle.
2. Draw an X on the animal above the bee.
3. Draw a circle around the object on the bottom.
4. Draw a triangle to the right of the fish. Draw a square to the left of the fish.

Chapter 7

Name

Chapter Pretest

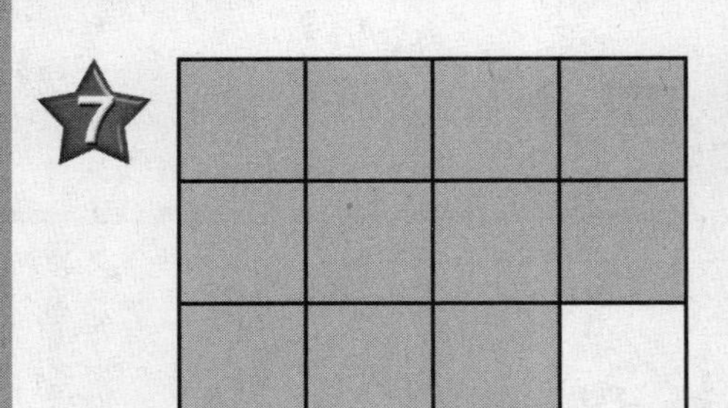
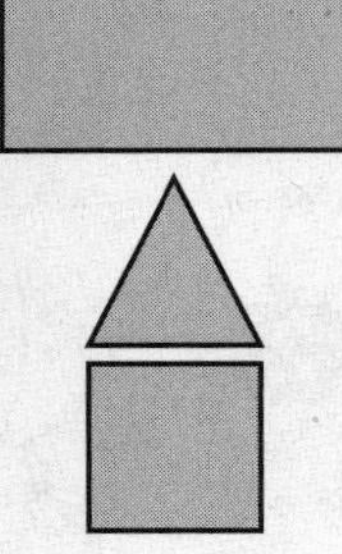

Directions:

5. Circle the pictures that show the back of a cat.
6. Draw an X outside the barn.
7. Draw an X on the object that fills the space.
8. Draw a circle around the butterfly before the flower.

Chapter Pretest

Scoring Guide and Diagnostic Chart

Students missing Exercise . . .	Have trouble with . . .	Should review . . .
1	Before or After	Chapter 7, Lesson 1
2	Above or Below	Chapter 7, Lesson 2
3	Top, Middle, or Bottom	Chapter 7, Lesson 3
4	Left or Right	Chapter 7, Lesson 4
5	Front or Back	Chapter 7, Lesson 5
6	Inside or Outside	Chapter 7, Lesson 6
7	Solve Puzzles	Chapter 7, Lesson 7
8	Before or After	Chapter 7, Lesson 1

Name

Chapter Test

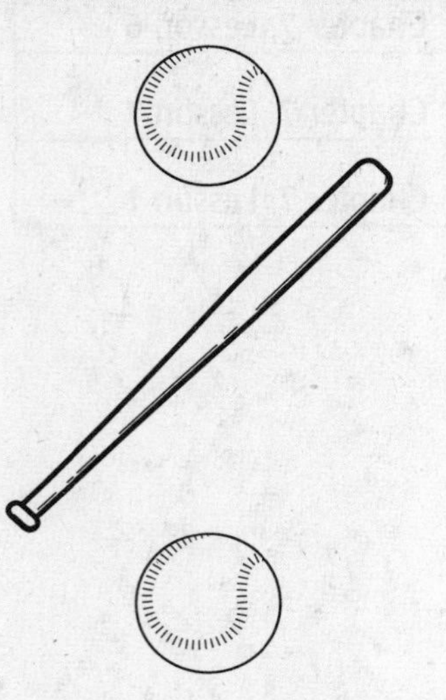

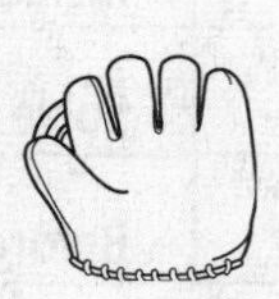

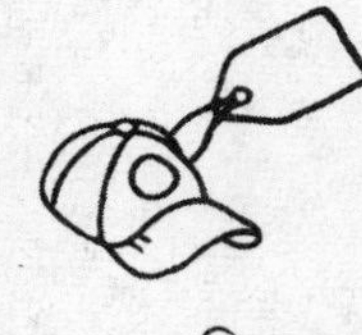

Directions:

1. Draw a circle around the object after the bike.
2. Draw an X on the object below the bat.
3. Draw a circle around the object on the top.
4. Draw a square to the right of the basketball hoop. Draw a triangle to the left of the basketball hoop.

Chapter 7

Name ______________________________

Chapter Test

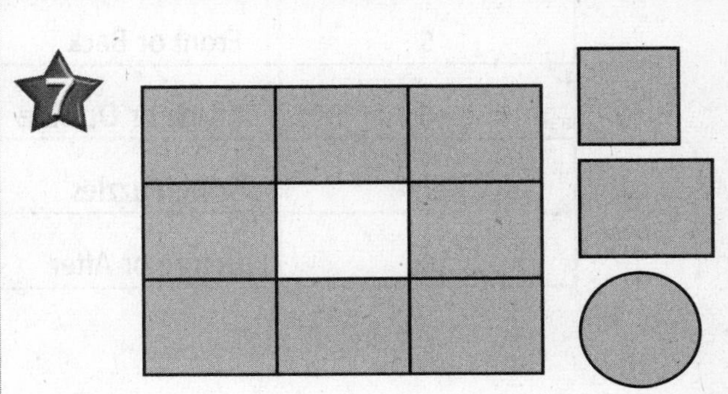

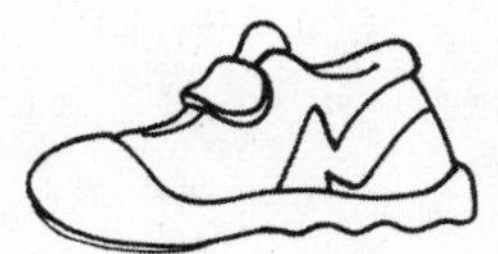

Directions:

5. Circle the pictures that show the back of a monkey.
6. Draw an X outside the bus.
7. Draw an X on the object that fills the space.
8. Draw a circle around the object that comes just after the baseball.

Chapter 7

Chapter Test

Scoring Guide and Diagnostic Chart

Students missing Exercise . . .	Have trouble with . . .	Should review . . .
1	Before or After	Chapter 7, Lesson 1
2	Above or Below	Chapter 7, Lesson 2
3	Top, Middle, or Bottom	Chapter 7, Lesson 3
4	Left or Right	Chapter 7, Lesson 4
5	Front or Back	Chapter 7, Lesson 5
6	Inside or Outside	Chapter 7, Lesson 6
7	Solve Puzzles	Chapter 7, Lesson 7
8	Before or After	Chapter 7, Lesson 1

Chapter 7

Name

Test Practice

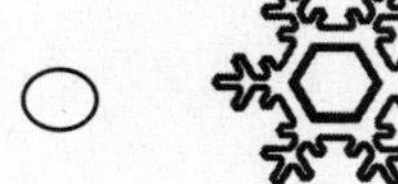

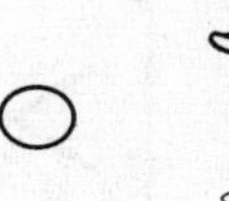

Directions:

1. Which object comes before the airplane?
2. Which object is above the snowflake?
3. Which object is below the duck?
4. Which picture shows the horse in the middle?

Chapter 7

Name ______________________

Test Practice

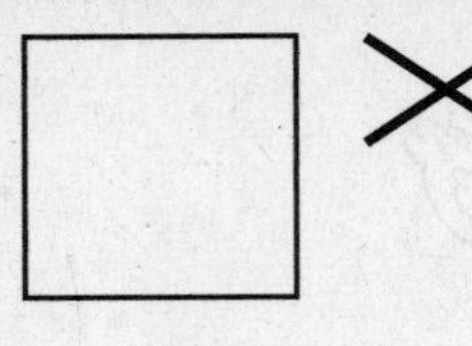   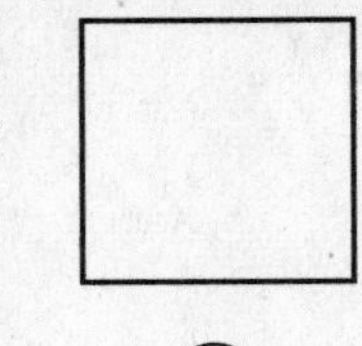

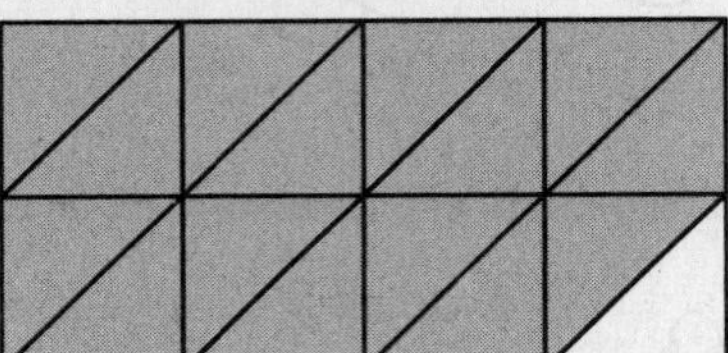

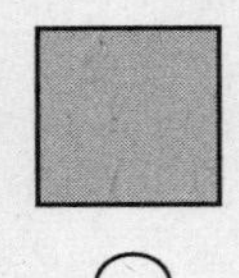 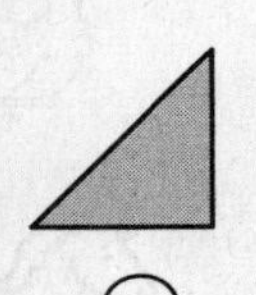 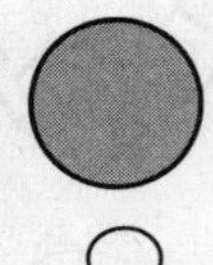

Directions:

4. Which picture shows the cloud to the right of the sun?
5. Which shows an X inside the square?
6. Which figure will fill the space?
7. Which shows the back of the bear?

Performance Assessment

CHILD'S TASK: Students identify animals in complete sentences using position words–*before, after, left, right, inside*, and *outside*.

Teacher Preparation/Instructions:

- Place an empty shoebox at the right end of a table.
- Place five different plastic farm animals in a row–all facing the shoebox; for example, you could use a cow, a horse, a sheep, a pig, and a chicken. If animals are not available in the classroom, you may use sketches or other illustrations.
- Then, use the questions for students to respond in complete sentences.

A. Steps for Assessment

Ask the following questions:

- *Which animal is before the pig?*
- *Which animal is after the horse?*
- *Which animal is just to the left of the sheep?*
- *Which animal is just to the right of the sheep?*

Teacher Preparation/Instructions:

- Place the pig and the horse inside the shoebox.
- Place the sheep, the chicken, and the cow outside the shoebox.
- Then, use the questions for students to answer in complete sentences.

B. Steps for Assessment

Ask: *Is the chicken inside the shoebox or outside the shoebox?* Repeat four more times, each time with the name of a different animal; for example, pig, inside; sheep, outside; horse, inside; cow, outside.

Chapter 7

Performance Assessment Teacher's Notes

Target Skills

- Identify objects using position words–*before, after, left, right, inside*, and *outside*.

Task Description

Students identify animals in complete sentences using position words–*before, after, left, right, inside*, and *outside*.

Teacher Notes

- Prompt students with sentence frames as necessary.

Scoring Rubric	
Score	Explanation
3	Students demonstrate an efficient strategy that enables them to solve the problem completely. Students will: • correctly point out each animal in the position specified. • correctly identify the position in a complete oral sentence.
2	Students demonstrate a strategy that enables them to solve the problem correctly. The strategy is disorganized or less efficient. Students may: • have to place their hands on the animals and name them while thinking aloud prior to giving a response. • identify the positions as first, next, and last prior to correctly identifying the positions.
1	Students demonstrate a confused strategy that leads to difficulty in solving the problem. Most answers are incorrect, but students demonstrate knowledge of at least one concept. Students may: • be unable to identify the animal's position. • be unable to complete an oral sentence.

Name

Section Test (Chapters 5–7)

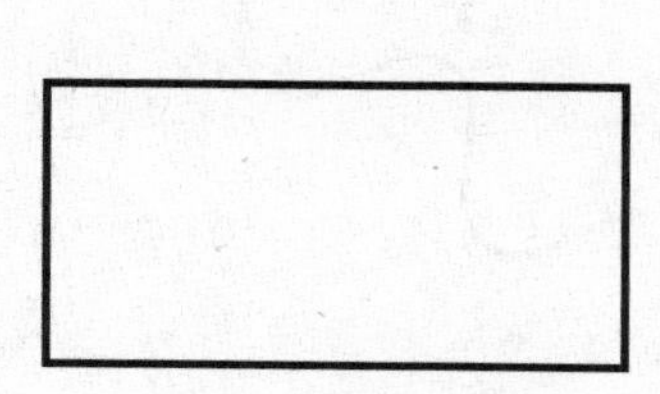 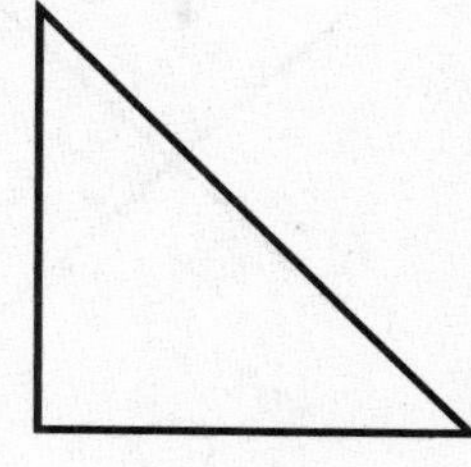 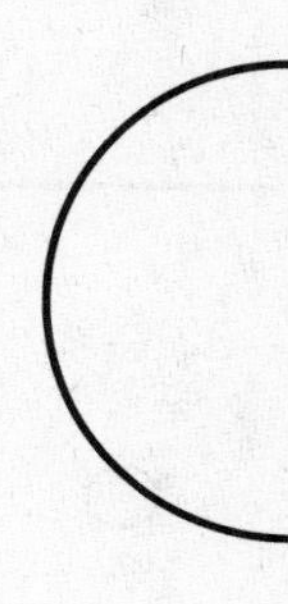

0 3 4

3

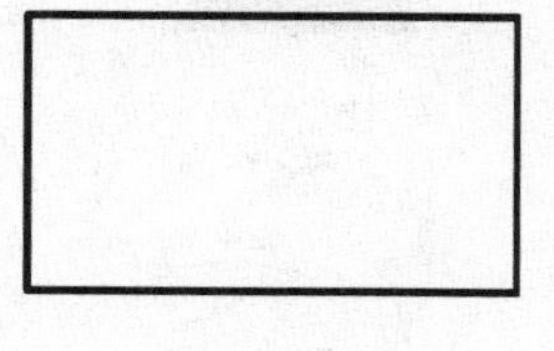 

Section Test

Name

Section Test (Chapters 5–7)

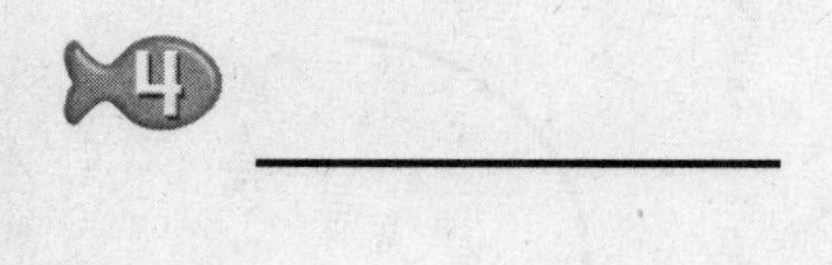

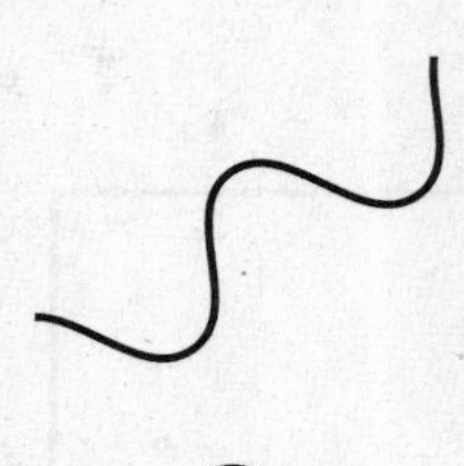

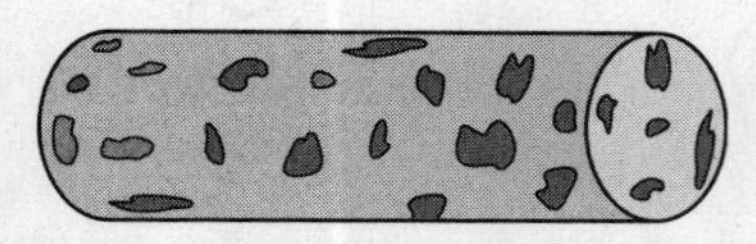
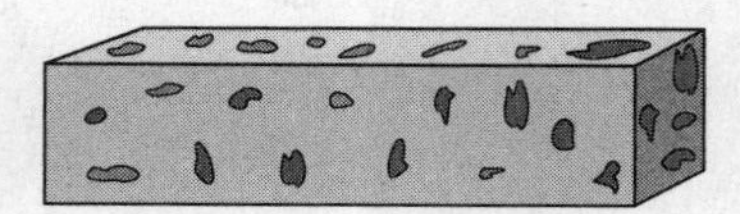

Section Test (Chapters 5–7)

Scoring Guide and Diagnostic Chart

Students missing Exercise . . .	Have trouble with . . .	Should review . . .
1	Open or Closed Figures	Chapter 5, Lesson 1
2	Triangles	Chapter 5, Lesson 4
3	Create Two-Dimensional Figures	Chapter 5, Lesson 7
4	Curved or Straight	Chapter 5, Lesson 2
5	Roll and Stack	Chapter 6, Lesson 2
6	Cylinders	Chapter 6, Lesson 4
7	Top, Middle, or Bottom	Chapter 7, Lesson 3

Teacher Directions

Read the following directions to students before they begin. Then, read each question followed by a pause to allow students time to work and choose an answer.

- **Write your name at the top of the page.**
- **I am going to read each question to you. Listen carefully before you choose an answer.**

1. Which is an open figure?
2. How many sides are in the figure?
3. Which figure would the smaller figures make?

- **Turn the page over.**

4. Which is a straight line?
5. Which object can be stacked?
6. Which object is a cylinder?
7. Which pictures shows the mountain at the bottom?

Section Test

Name

Section Pretest (Chapters 8–10)

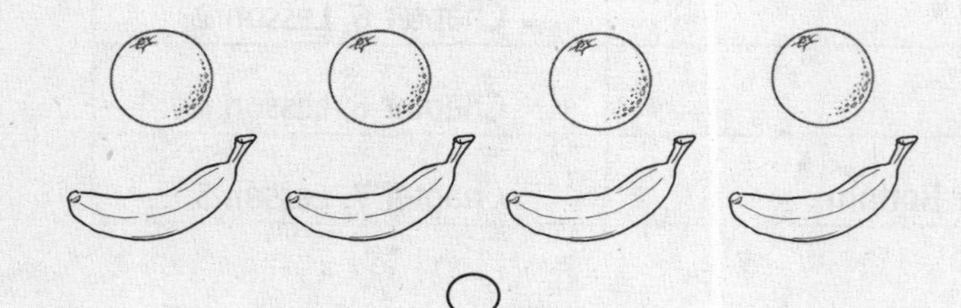

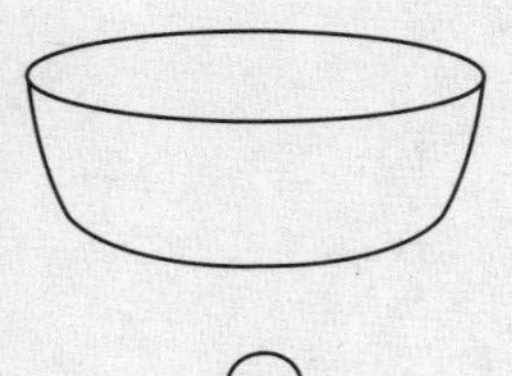

Name

Section Pretest (Chapters 8–10)

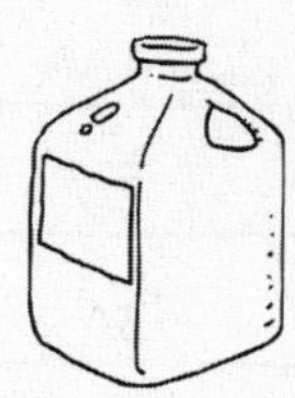

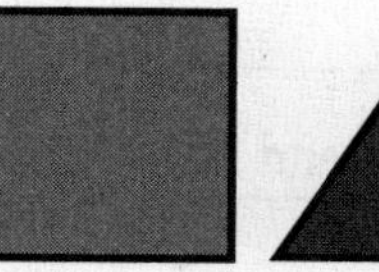

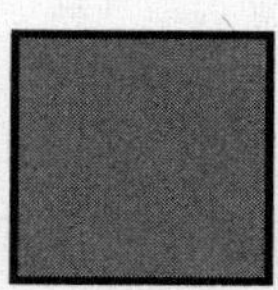

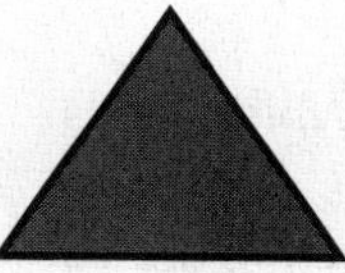

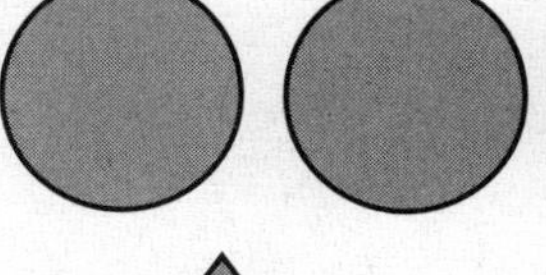

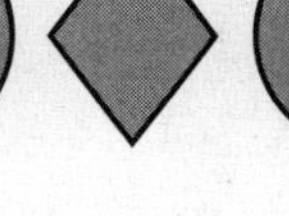

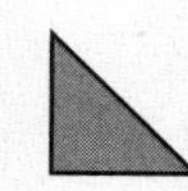

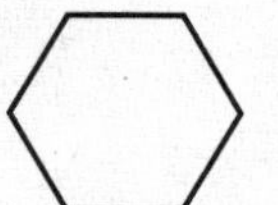
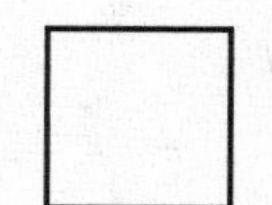

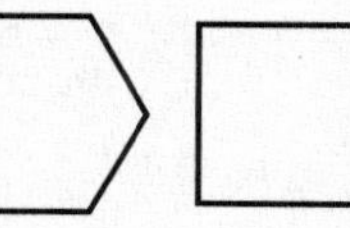
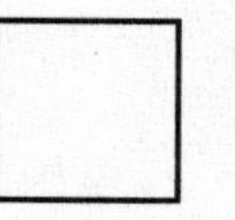

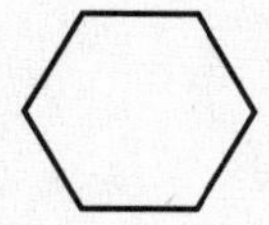

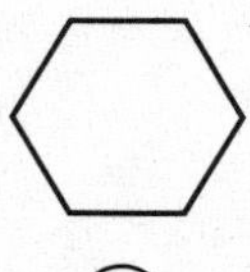
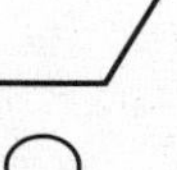
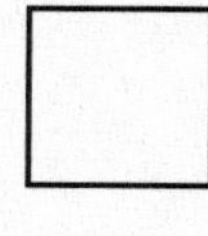
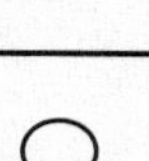

Section Pretest

Section Pretest (Chapters 8–10)
Scoring Guide and Diagnostic Chart

Students missing Exercise . . .	Have trouble with . . .	Should review . . .
1	Equal or Unequal	Chapter 8, Lesson 2
2	Full or Empty	Chapter 8, Lesson 7
3	Heavy or Heavier	Chapter 9, Lesson 4
4	More and Most	Chapter 9, Lesson 6
5	AB Patterns	Chapter 10, Lesson 2
6	AAB Patterns	Chapter 10, Lesson 3
7	Identify and Extend Patterns	Chapter 10, Lesson 6

Teacher Directions

Read the following directions to students before they begin. Then, read each question followed by a pause to allow students time to work and choose an answer.

- **Write your name at the top of the page.**
- **I am going to read each question to you. Listen carefully before you choose an answer.**

1. Which shows the same number of oranges and bananas?
2. Which fruit bowl is empty?
3. Which object is heavier than the apple?

- **Turn the page over.**

4. Look at the containers. Which holds the most?
5. Look at the pattern. Which figure comes next in the pattern?
6. Look at the pattern. Which figure comes next?
7. Look at the pattern. Which figure comes next?

Chapter 8

Name

Chapter Pretest

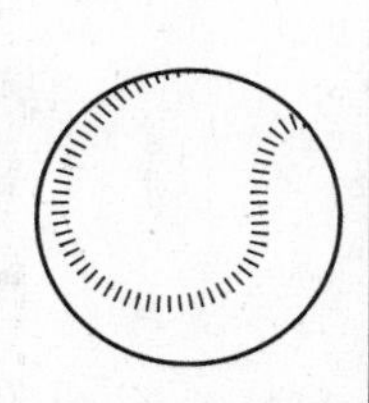

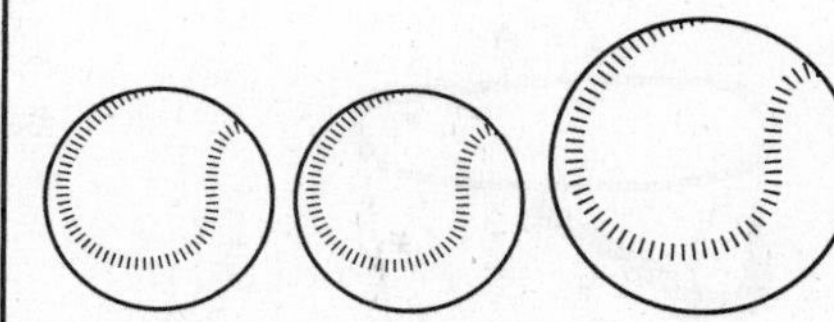

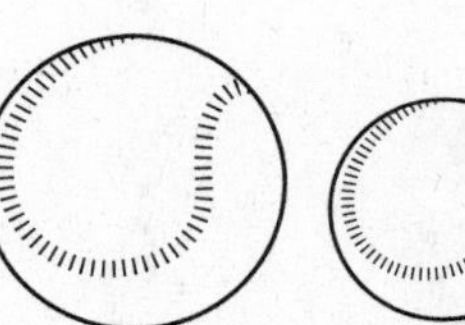

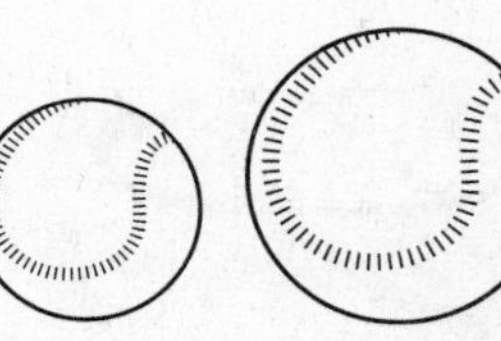

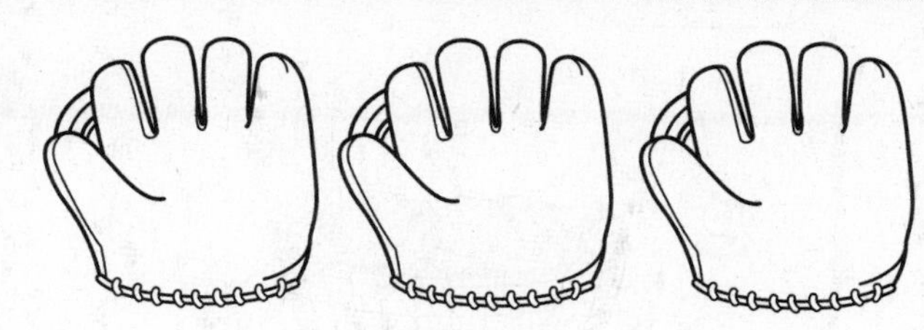

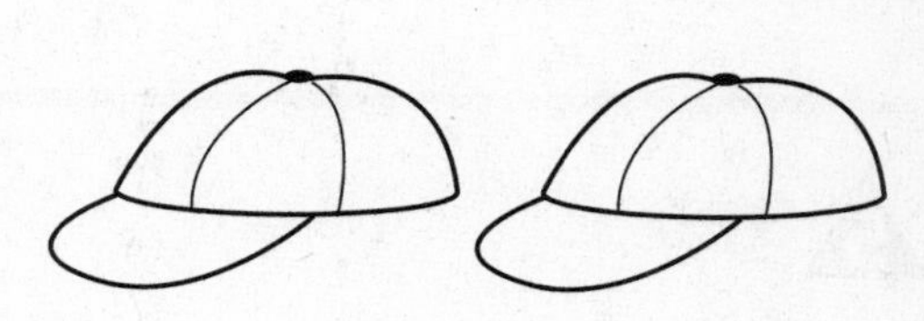

Yes No

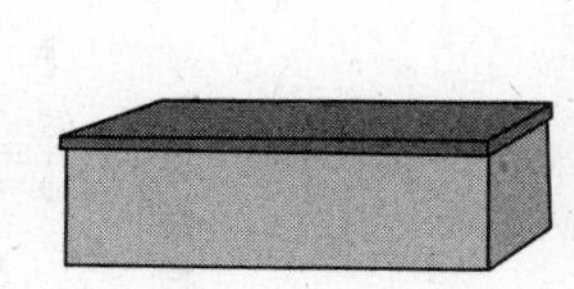

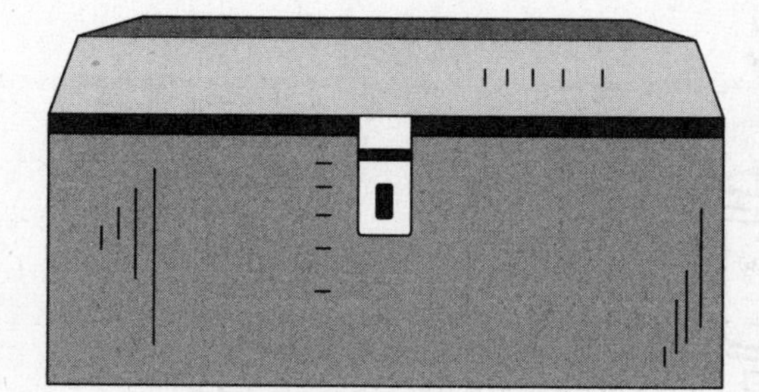

Chapter 8

Directions:

1. Look at the first ball. Circle the balls that are the same size as the first ball. Draw an X on the balls that are a different size.
2. Count the mitts. Write how many. Count the caps. Write how many. Is the number of mitts equal to the number of caps? Circle Yes or No.
3. The box holds 6 balls. The chest holds 60 balls. Put an X on the container that holds more.

Name ______________________

Chapter Pretest

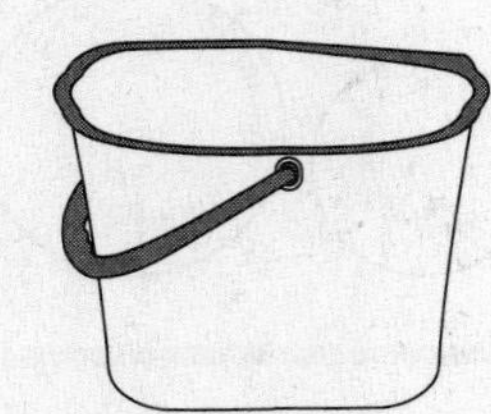

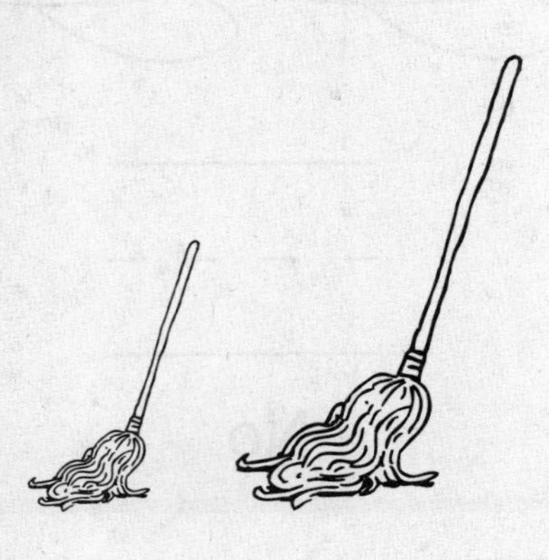

Directions:

4. Draw an X on the empty bucket.
5. Circle the tall mop.
6. Jan and Adam are helping their dad wash the clothes. They are filling the basket shown. Draw a basket that will hold less than the basket Jan and Adam are using.
7. Circle the light object. Draw an X on the heavy object.

Chapter 8

Chapter Pretest

Scoring Guide and Diagnostic Chart

Students missing Exercise . . .	Have trouble with . . .	Should review . . .
1	Same or Different	Chapter 8, Lesson 1
2	Equal or Unequal	Chapter 8, Lesson 2
3	More or Less	Chapter 8, Lesson 3
4	Full or Empty	Chapter 8, Lesson 7
5	Tall or Short	Chapter 8, Lesson 5
6	More or Less	Chapter 8, Lesson 3
7	Heavy or Light	Chapter 8, Lesson 6

Chapter 8

Name

Chapter Test

1

2

Yes No

3

Directions:

1. Look at the first flowerpot. Circle the flowerpots that are the same size as the one shown. Put an X on the flowerpots that are a different size.
2. Count the flowers. Write how many. Count the trees. Write how many. Is the number of flowers equal to the number of trees? Circle Yes or No.
3. The bottle holds 2 flowers. The pitcher holds 20 flowers. Put an X on the container that holds less.

Name ________________________________

Chapter Test

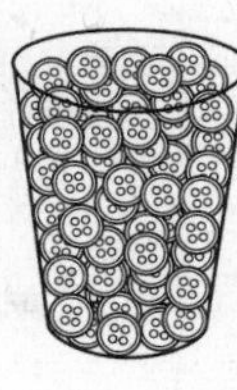

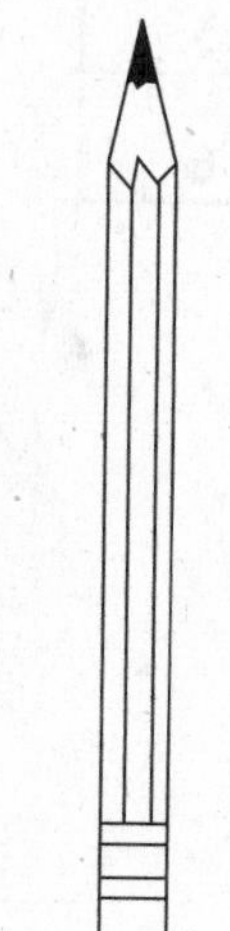

Directions:

4. Draw an X on the full cup.
5. Circle the short pencil.
6. Raj and Pat are helping their grandparents make some scarves. Raj and Pat are filling the box shown with things their grandparents will need. Draw a box that will hold more than the box Raj and Pat are using.
7. Circle the light object. Draw an X on the heavy object.

Chapter 8

Chapter Test

Scoring Guide and Diagnostic Chart

Students missing Exercise . . .	Have trouble with . . .	Should review . . .
1	Same or Different	Chapter 8, Lesson 1
2	Equal or Unequal	Chapter 8, Lesson 2
3	More or Less	Chapter 8, Lesson 3
4	Full or Empty	Chapter 8, Lesson 7
5	Tall or Short	Chapter 8, Lesson 5
6	More or Less	Chapter 8, Lesson 3
7	Heavy or Light	Chapter 8, Lesson 6

Chapter 8

Name

Test Practice

1

○

○

○

2

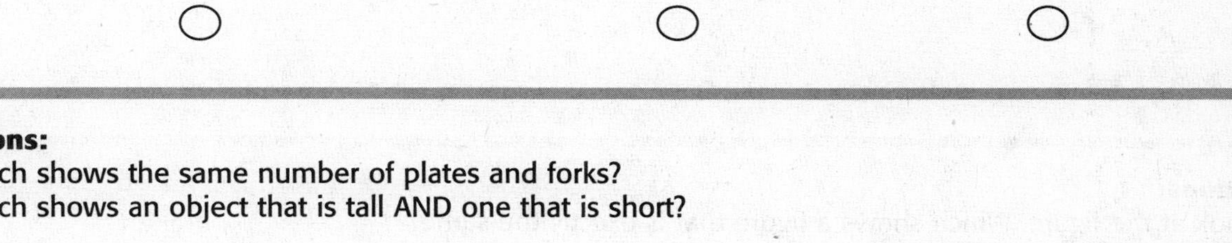

○ ○ ○

Directions:

1. Which shows the same number of plates and forks?
2. Which shows an object that is tall AND one that is short?

Chapter 8

Name ______________________

Test Practice

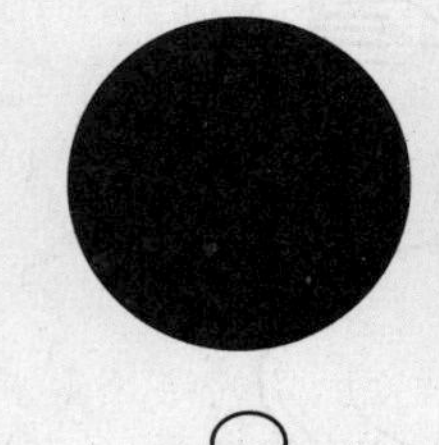

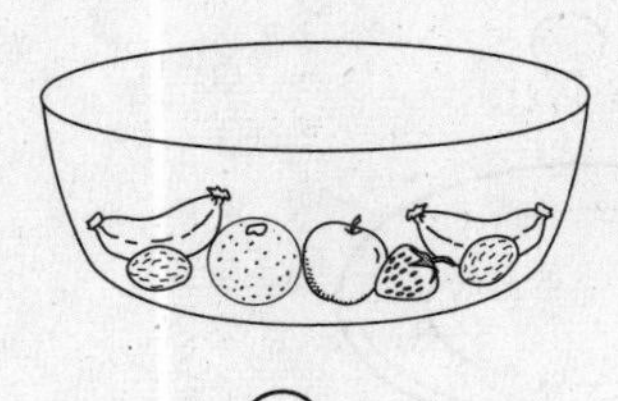
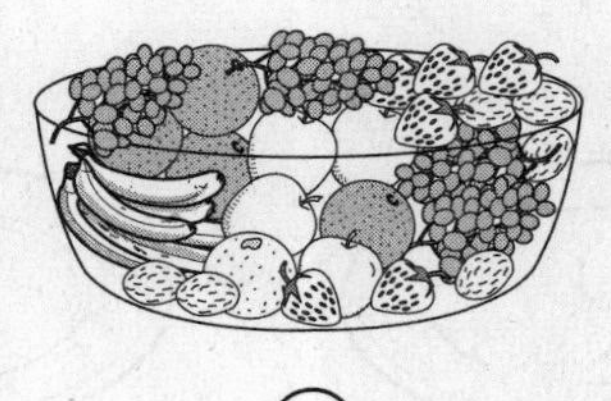

Directions:

3. Look at the figure. Which shows a figure that is exactly the same?
4. Which bowl is empty?
5. Which is the heavy object?

Chapter 8

Performance Assessment

CHILD'S TASK: Students identify groups that are the same or different, equal or unequal; and determine items that are full or empty.

Teacher Preparation/Instructions:

- Place 4 red chenille sticks inside an unsealed envelope and 5 blue counters inside a second unsealed envelope.
- Place both envelopes and an empty envelope into a shoebox.
- Then place three mats in a row on a table. On the first mat place nothing; on the middle mat, a group of 5 red chenille sticks; and on the third mat, a group of 4 blue counters.

ONE WAY:

1. Look at the group of counters and the group of chenille sticks on the table. Ask: "Is the number of counters equal to the number of sticks?"
2. Give student the empty envelope from the shoebox. Ask: "Is this envelope full or empty?"
3. Choose an envelope from the shoebox. Take the items out of the envelope and place them on the first mat.
4. Point to the items on the first mat. Say: "This is your group. What color are the items in your group? Point to the group that has only items that are the same color as items in your group."
5. Again, point to the items on the first mat. Say: "This is your group. How many items are in your group? Point to the group that has the same number of items as the number of items in your group."

ANOTHER WAY TO PLAY: Place only two empty mats on the table. Provide a variety of colors of chenille sticks and counters. Have students choose an envelope, place the items on a mat, and then use the other mat to create a group that matches in number or color.

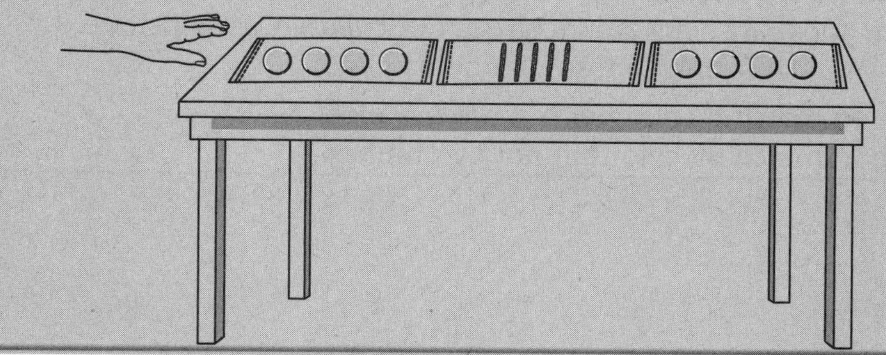

Chapter 8

Performance Assessment Teacher's Notes

Target Skills

- Identify groups that are the same or different.
- Identify groups that are equal or unequal.
- Determine whether an item is full or empty.

Task Description

Students identify groups that are the same or different, equal or unequal; and determine items that are full or empty.

Teacher Notes

- Model an example before children begin to play.

Scoring Rubric	
Score	Explanation
3	Student demonstrate an efficient strategy that enables them to solve the problem completely. Students will: • correctly recognize and state whether the envelope is full or empty. • correctly identify a set that matches in color. • correctly identify a set that matches in number.
2	Students demonstrate a strategy that enables them to solve the problem correctly. The strategy is disorganized or less efficient. Students may: • initially be inclined to match sets either by number when asked to match by color or by color when asked to identify by number; however, students will ultimately make the correct match. • be confused by the meaning of the word "equal" but ultimately identify the set that is equal to the given set.
1	Student demonstrate a confused strategy that leads to difficulty in solving the problem. Most answers are incorrect, but children demonstrate knowledge of at least one concept. Students may: • be able to match by number but not by color. • be able to match by color but not by number.

Chapter 9

Name ______________________

Chapter Pretest

1

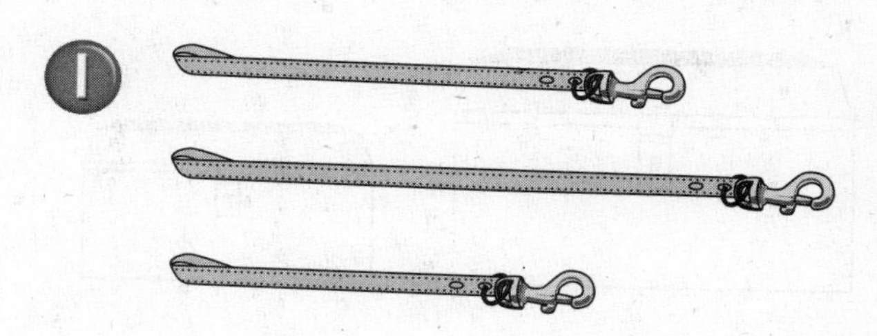

2

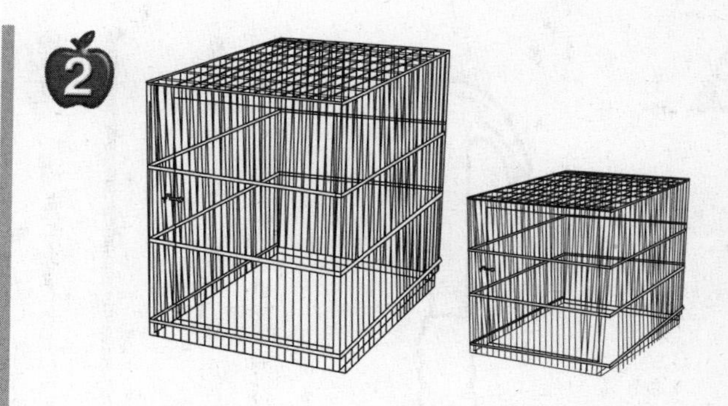

3

4

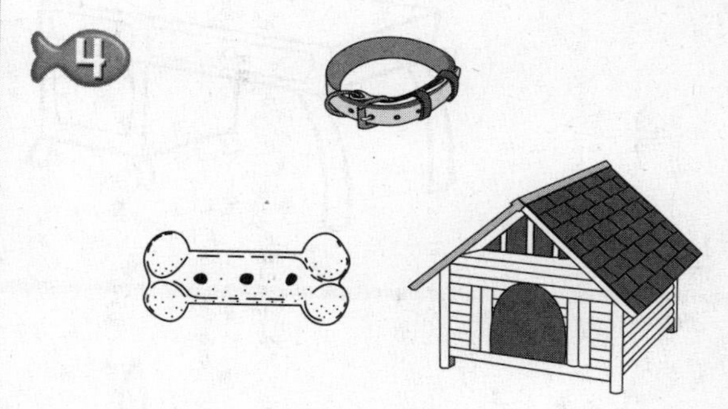

Directions:

1. Circle the longest leash.
2. Draw an X on the taller dog crate.
3. Circle the shortest dog.
4. Draw an X on the item that is heavier than the collar.

Name ____________________

Chapter Pretest

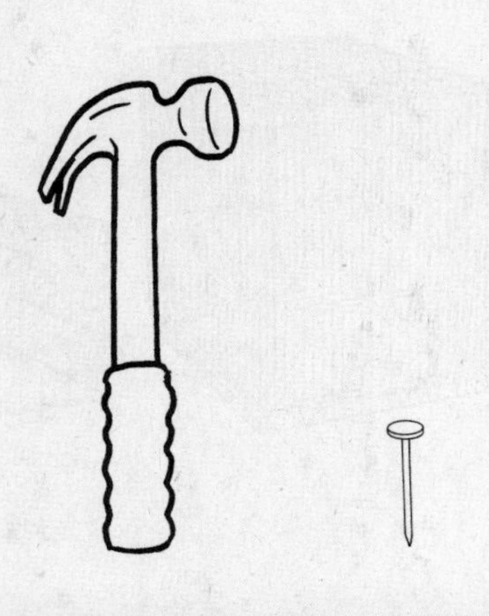

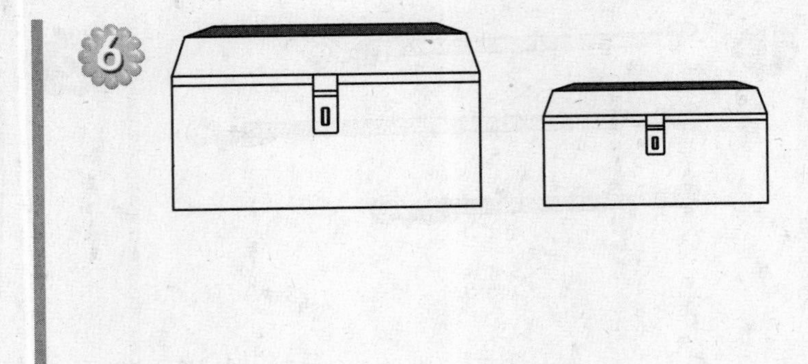

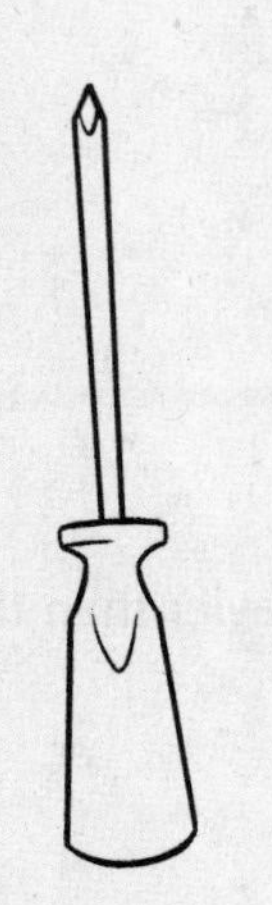

Directions:

5. Circle the lighter object.
6. Circle the item that holds more.
7. Circle the item that holds the least.
8. Draw an X on the tallest object.

Chapter 9

Chapter Pretest

Scoring Guide and Diagnostic Chart

Students missing Exercise . . .	Have trouble with . . .	Should review . . .
1	Long, Longer, Longest	Chapter 9, Lesson 1
2	Tall, Taller, Tallest	Chapter 9, Lesson 2
3	Short, Shorter, Shortest	Chapter 9, Lesson 3
4	Heavy or Heavier	Chapter 9, Lesson 4
5	Light or Lighter	Chapter 9, Lesson 5
6	More and Most	Chapter 9, Lesson 6
7	Less and Least	Chapter 9, Lesson 7
8	Tall, Taller, Tallest	Chapter 9, Lesson 2

Chapter 9

Name

Chapter Test

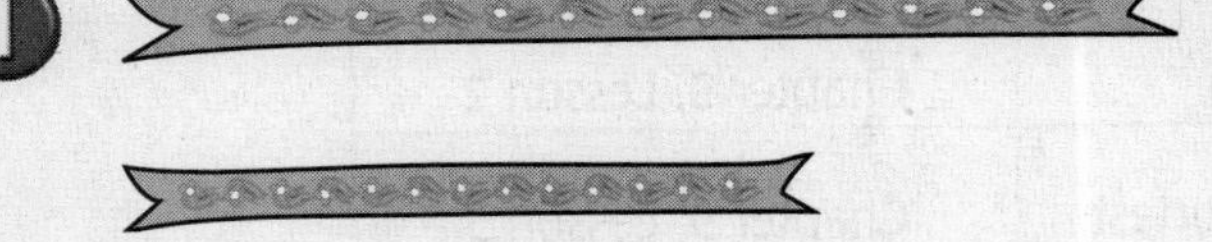

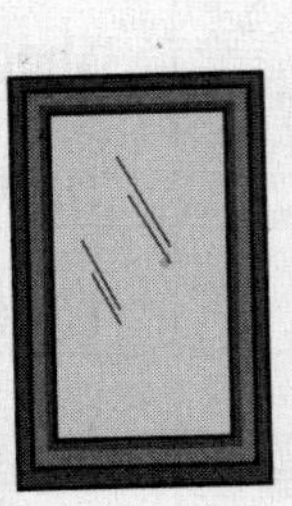
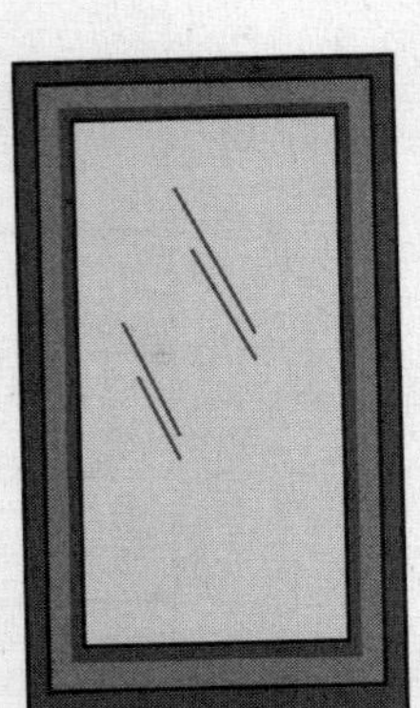

3

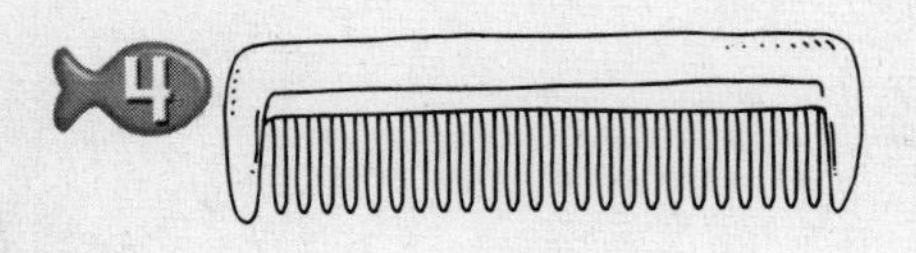

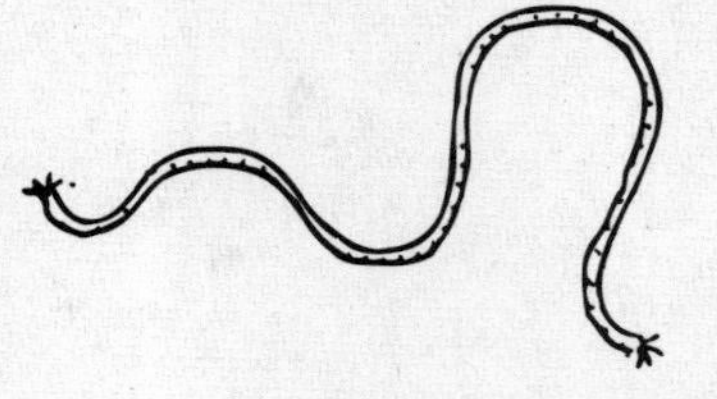

Directions:

1. Circle the ribbon that is longer.
2. Draw an X on the mirror that is taller.
3. Circle the shortest bottle.
4. Draw an X on the item that is heavier than the comb.

Chapter 9

Name

Chapter Test

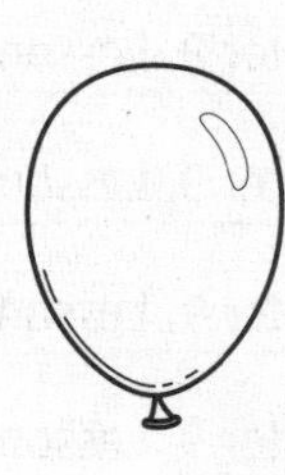

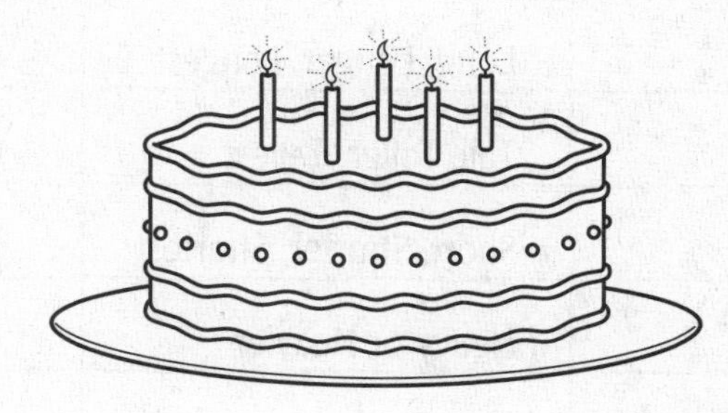

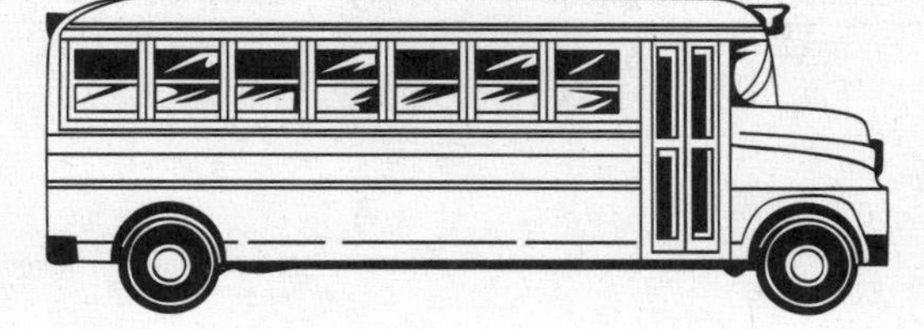

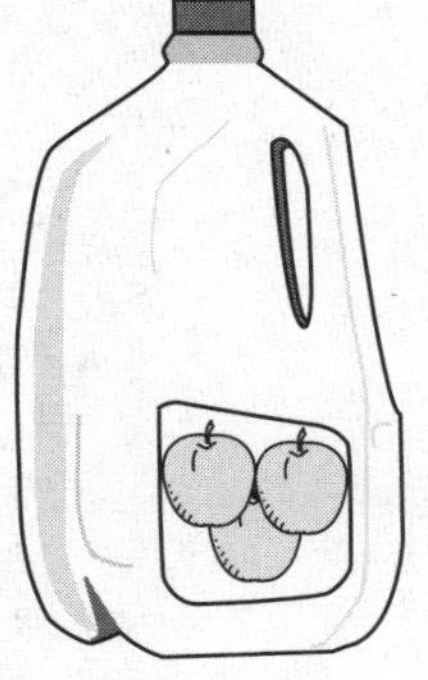

Directions:

5. Circle the lighter object.
6. Circle the item that holds the most people.
7. Draw an X on the item that holds less.
8. Draw an X on the tallest object.

Chapter 9

Chapter Test

Scoring Guide and Diagnostic Chart

Students missing Exercise . . .	Have trouble with . . .	Should review . . .
1	Long, Longer, Longest	Chapter 9, Lesson 1
2	Tall, Taller, Tallest	Chapter 9, Lesson 2
3	Short, Shorter, Shortest	Chapter 9, Lesson 3
4	Heavy or Heavier	Chapter 9, Lesson 4
5	Light or Lighter	Chapter 9, Lesson 5
6	More and Most	Chapter 9, Lesson 6
7	Less and Least	Chapter 9, Lesson 7
8	Tall, Taller, Tallest	Chapter 9, Lesson 2

Name

Test Practice

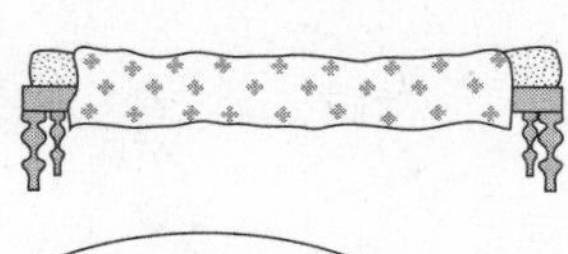

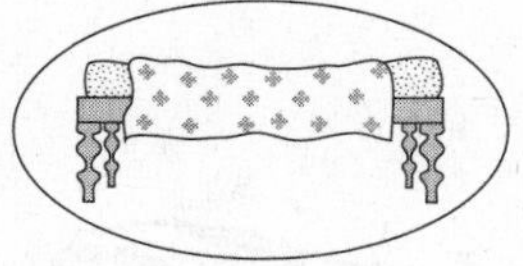

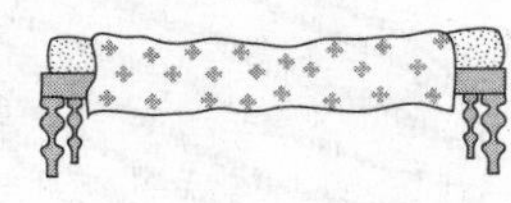

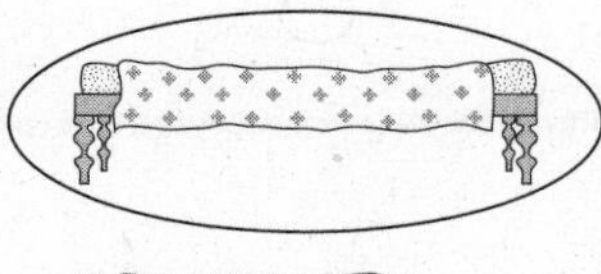

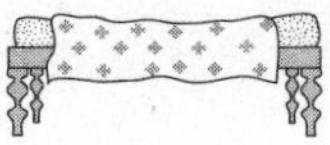

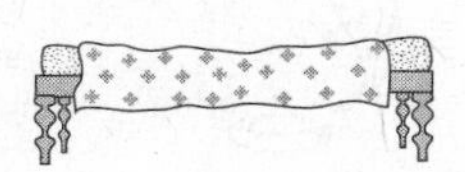

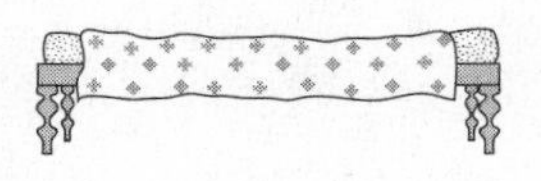

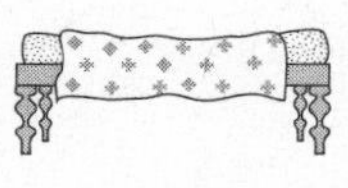

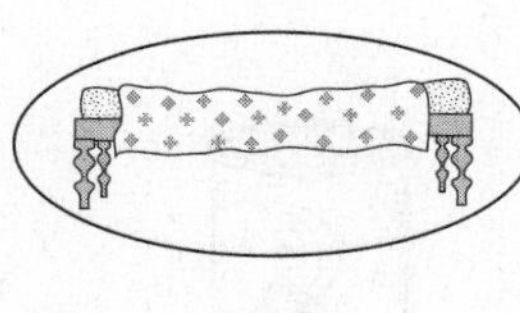

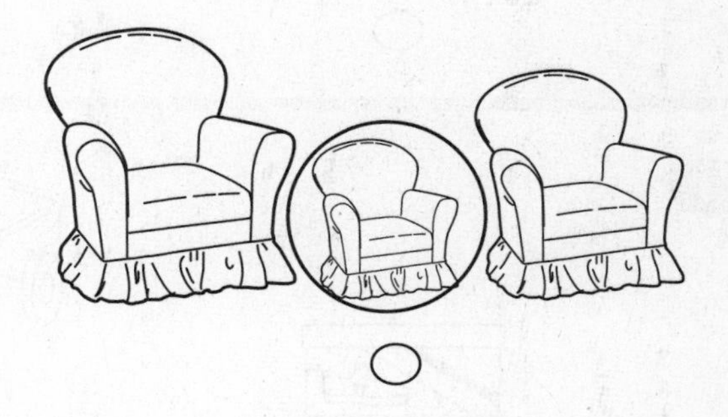

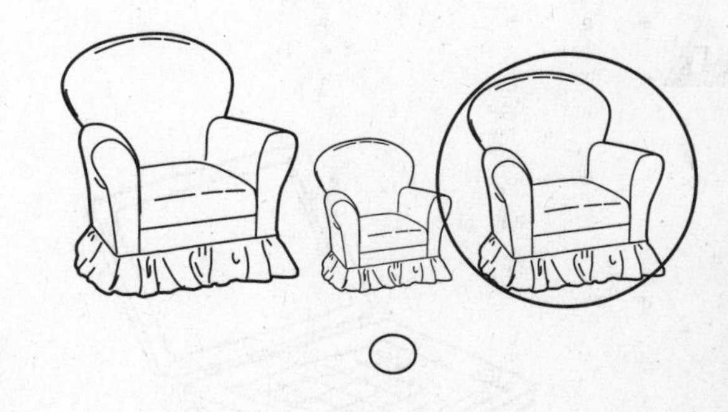

Directions:

1. Which group shows a circle around the longest bed?
2. Which group shows a circle around the tallest chair?

Chapter 9

Name ______________________

Test Practice

3

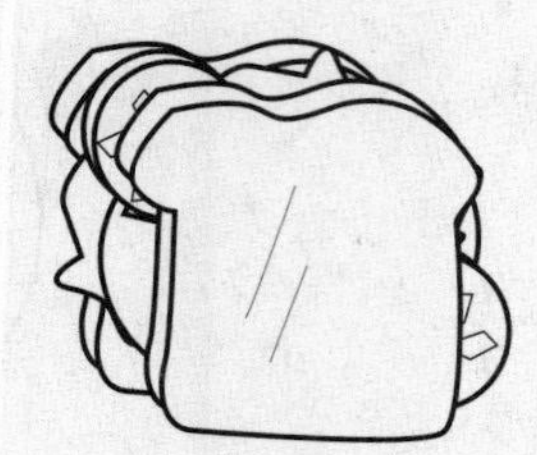

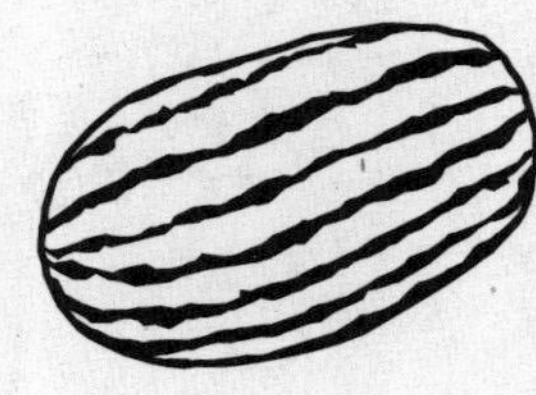

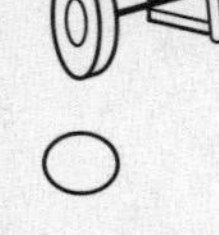

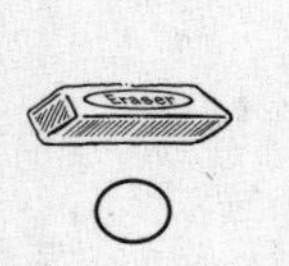

Directions:

3. Look at the sandwich. Which item is heavier than the sandwich?
4. Which item holds the most?
5. Look at the book. Which item is lighter than the book?

Chapter 9

Performance Assessment

CHILD'S TASK: Students will identify and describe items in four groups with the words *longest, shortest, tallest, most, least*, or *heavier*.

Teacher Preparation/Instructions

- Connect two chenille sticks to make a long "pointer."
- Place four mats on a table with the items listed below.

Mat 1: three pieces of chalk that are of different lengths—long, longer, longest
Mat 2: three plush or plastic animals of differing heights—tall, taller, tallest—and standing upright
Mat 3: small cup, medium glass, large pitcher
Mat 4: paperclip, chalk eraser, book

ONE WAY:

Tell children they will play a pointing game with the special pointer. Direct children to follow the steps below:

1. Look at Mat 1. Say: "Point to the piece of chalk that is the longest. Now, point to the piece of chalk that is the shortest."
2. Look at Mat 2. Say: "Point to the animal that is the tallest. Now, point to the animal that is the shortest."
3. Look at Mat 3. Say: "Point to the object that holds the most. Now, point to the object that holds the least."
4. Look at Mat 4. Say: "Without picking up these objects, point to the object that is heavier than the eraser."

ANOTHER WAY:

For Mat 1, provide the listed items next to the mat in no special order. Have students place the items on the mat in the order of long, longer, longest. Repeat with Mat 2 and tall, taller, tallest.

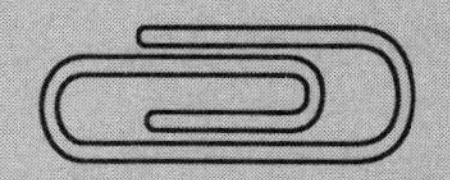

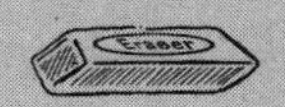

Chapter 9

Chapter 9

Performance Assessment Teacher's Notes

Target Skills

- Identify the shortest and longest objects in a group.
- Identify the tallest and shortest objects in a group.
- Identify the objects in a group that will hold the most and the least.
- Identify the object in a group that is heavier than another object in the group.

Task Description

Students will identify and describe items in four groups with the words *longest*, *shortest*, *tallest*, *most*, *least*, or *heavier*.

Teacher Notes

Model an example before students begin to play.

Scoring Rubric	
Score	Explanation
3	Students demonstrate an efficient strategy that enables them to solve the problem completely. Students will: • correctly identify longest and shortest items. • correctly identify tallest and shortest items. • correctly identify items that hold the most and the least. • correctly identify an item that is heavier than a specified item.
2	Students demonstrate a strategy that enables them to solve the problem correctly. The strategy is disorganized or less efficient. Students may: • initially be confused by the terms *longest* and *shortest* or *tallest* and *shortest* but ultimately make the correct choice. • initially be confused by the terms *most* and *least* or the word *heavier* but ultimately make the correct choice.
1	Students demonstrate a confused strategy that leads to difficulty in solving the problem. Most answers are incorrect, but students demonstrate knowledge of at least one concept. Students may: • be able to determine only one of the following: longest and shortest, tallest and shortest. • be able to determine only one of the following: least or most, heavier.

Name

Chapter Pretest

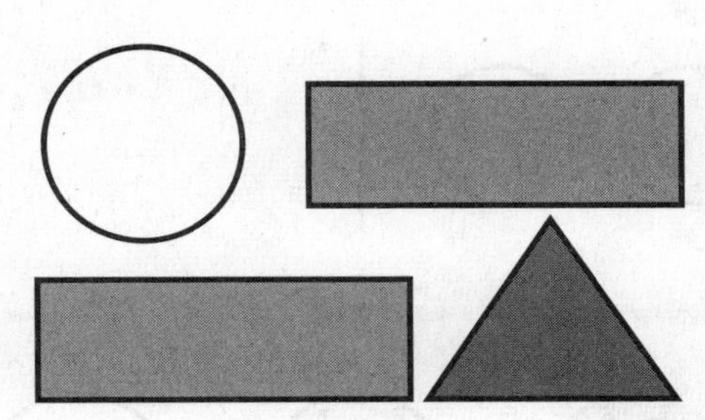
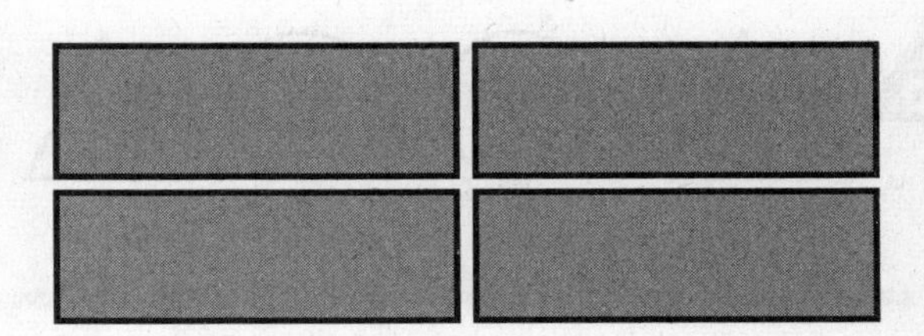

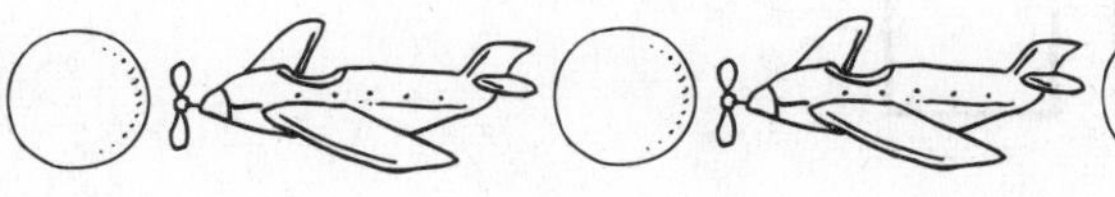
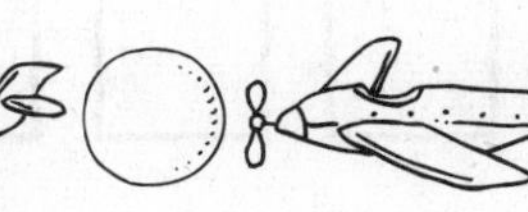
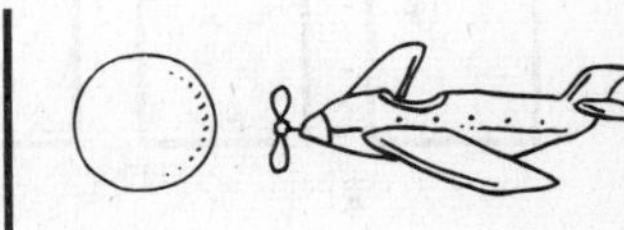

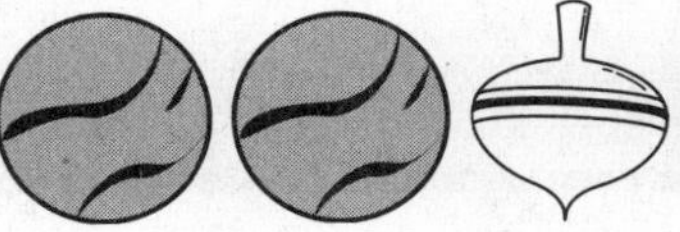
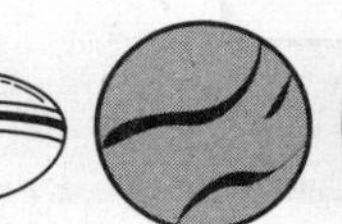
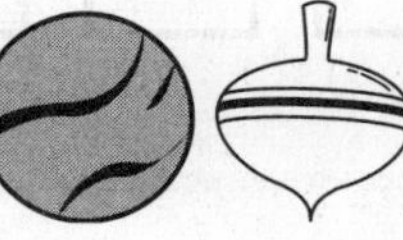
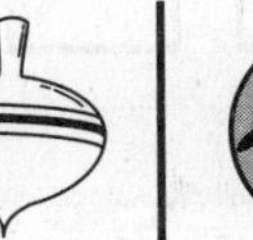
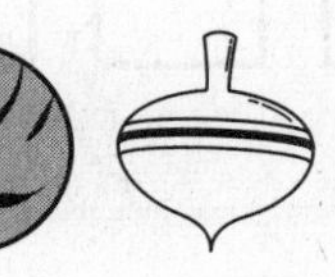

Directions:

1. Draw an X on the group that is the same size and shape.
2. Circle the toy that belongs in the group.
3. Circle what comes next in the pattern.
4. Circle what comes next in the pattern.

Chapter 10

Name ____________________

Chapter Pretest

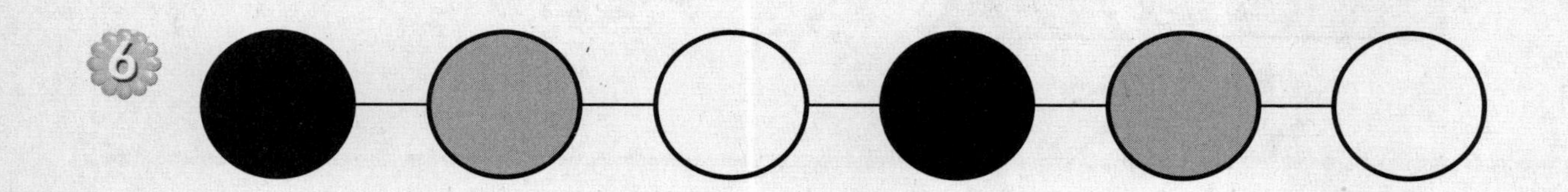

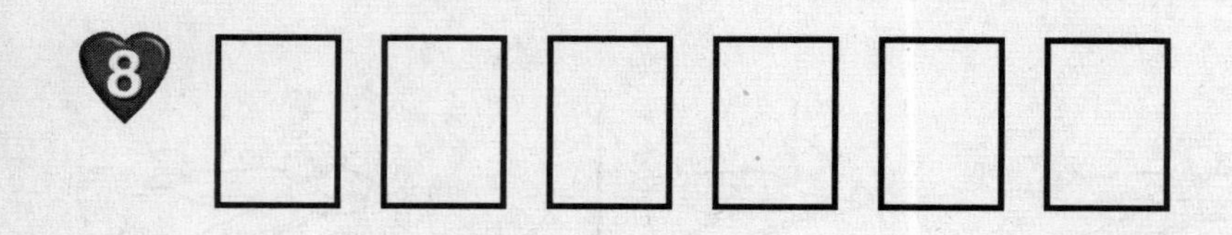

Directions:

5. Look at the pattern. Draw the shape that comes next.
6. Draw a line to show where the pattern starts over, or repeats.
7. Circle the picture that comes next.
8. Choose two numbers. Make an AB pattern.
9. Choose two letters. Make an ABB pattern.

Chapter Pretest

Scoring Guide and Diagnostic Chart

Students missing Exercise . . .	Have trouble with . . .	Should review . . .
1	More than One Attribute	Chapter 10, Lesson 1
2	More than One Attribute	Chapter 10, Lesson 1
3	AB Patterns	Chapter 10, Lesson 2
4	AAB Patterns	Chapter 10, Lesson 3
5	ABB Patterns	Chapter 10, Lesson 4
6	ABC Patterns	Chapter 10, Lesson 5
7	Identify and Extend Patterns	Chapter 10, Lesson 6
8	Create Patterns	Chapter 10, Lesson 7
9	Create Patterns	Chapter 10, Lesson 7

Chapter 10

Name

Chapter Test

1

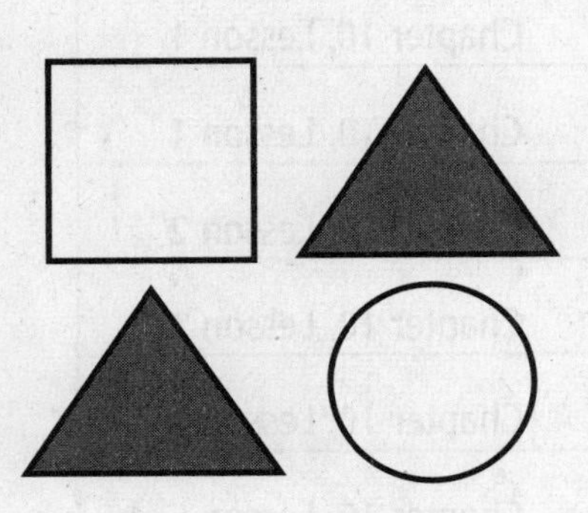

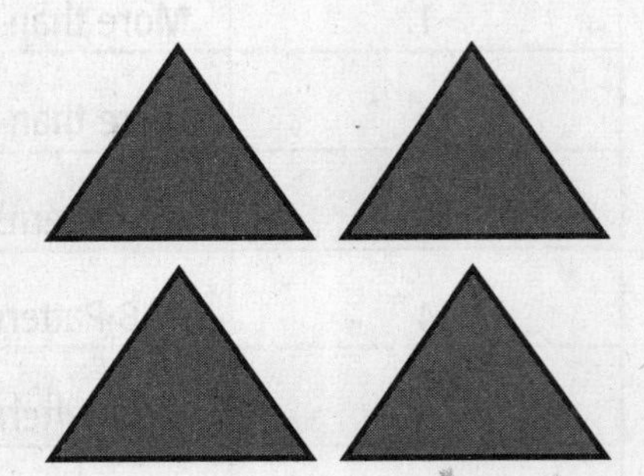

2

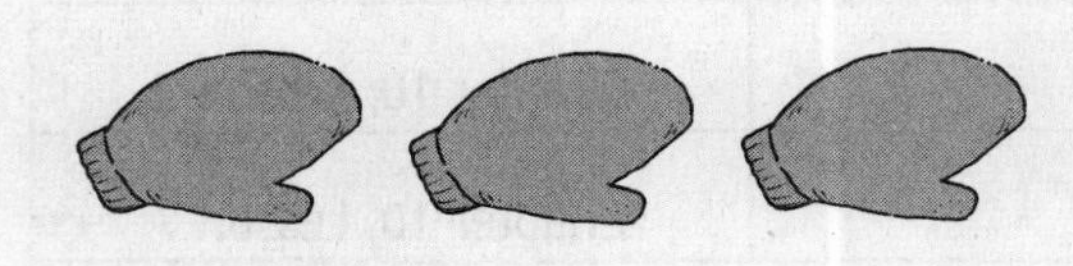

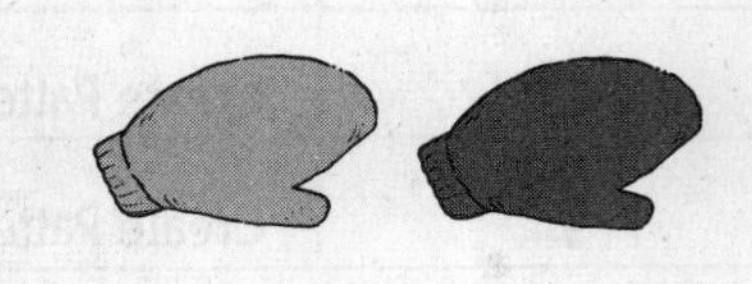

3

Directions:

1. Draw an X on the group that is the same size and shape.
2. Circle the item that belongs in the group.
3. Circle the picture that comes next.
4. Circle what comes next in the pattern.

Name

Chapter Test

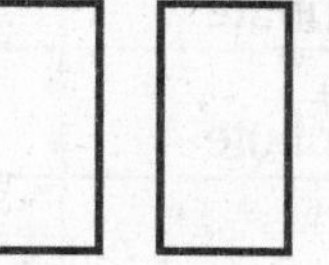

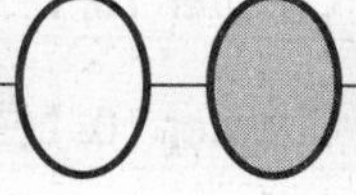
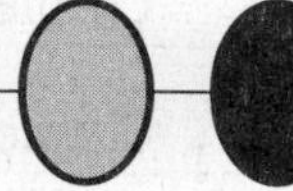
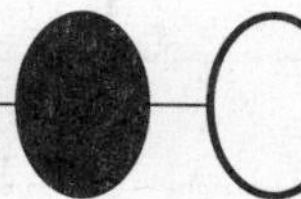

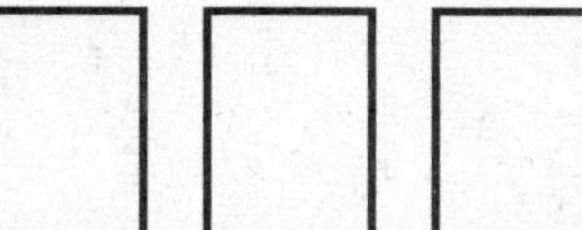
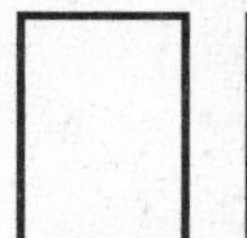
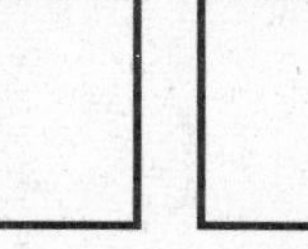
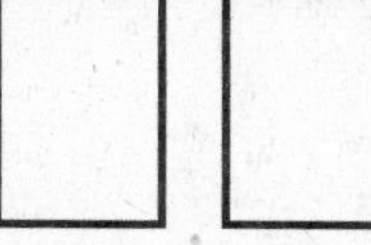

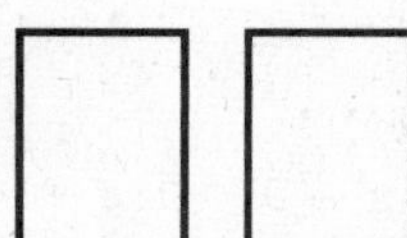

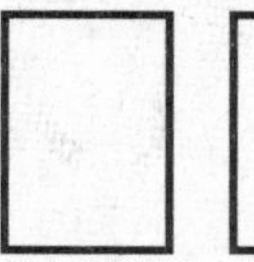
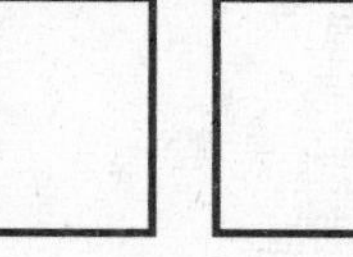

Directions:

5. Look at the pattern. Draw the next shape.
6. Draw a line to show where the pattern starts over, or repeats.
7. Circle what comes next in the pattern.
8. Choose two letters. Make an AB pattern.
9. Choose two numbers. Make an ABB pattern.

Chapter 10

Chapter Test

Scoring Guide and Diagnostic Chart

Students missing Exercise . . .	Have trouble with . . .	Should review . . .
1	More than One Attribute	Chapter 10, Lesson 1
2	More than One Attribute	Chapter 10, Lesson 1
3	AB Patterns	Chapter 10, Lesson 2
4	AAB Patterns	Chapter 10, Lesson 3
5	ABB Patterns	Chapter 10, Lesson 4
6	ABC Patterns	Chapter 10, Lesson 5
7	Identify and Extend Patterns	Chapter 10, Lesson 6
8	Create Patterns	Chapter 10, Lesson 7
9	Create Patterns	Chapter 10, Lesson 7

Name

Test Practice

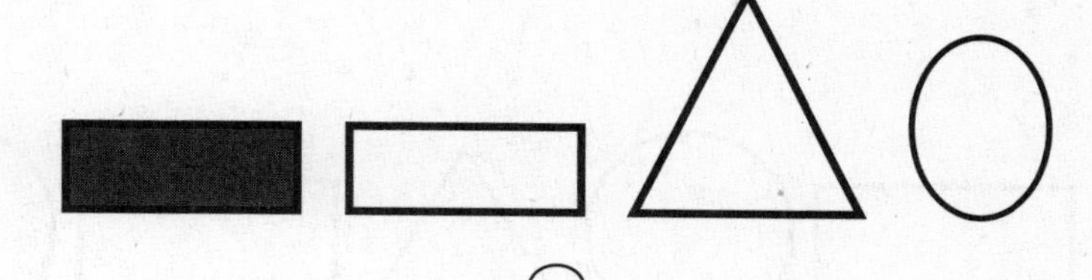

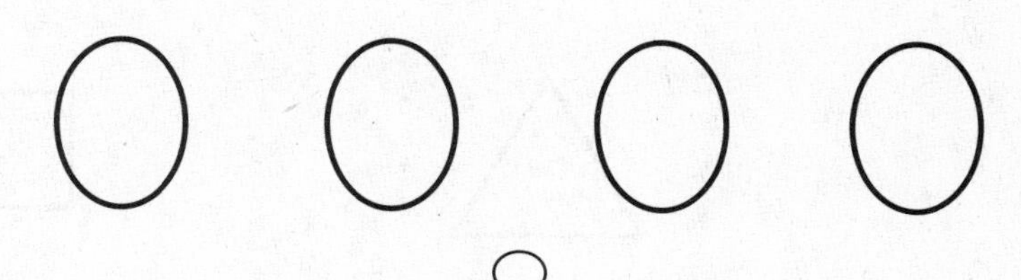

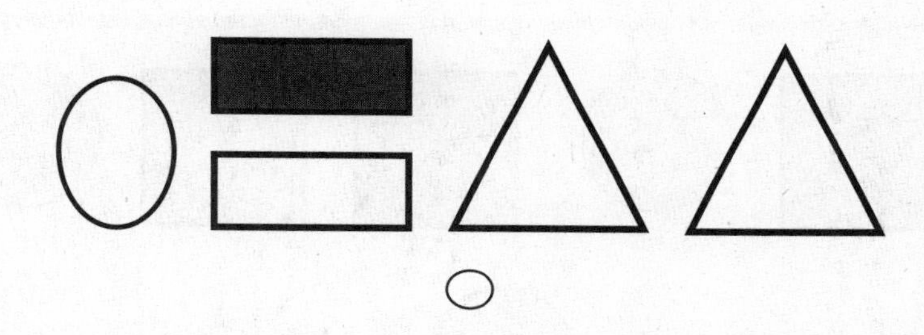

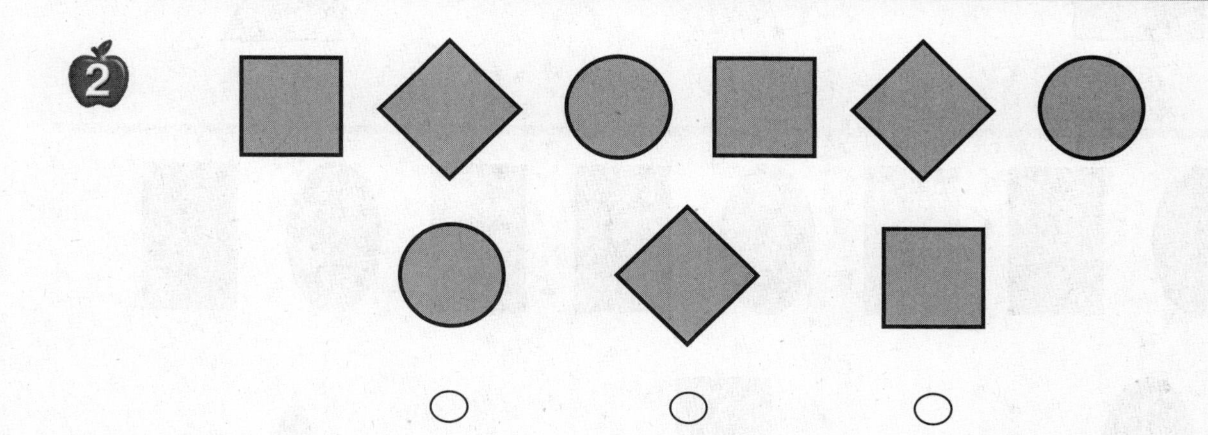

Directions:

1. Which group shows figures that are all the same size and shape?
2. What comes next in the pattern?

Chapter 10

Name

Test Practice

3

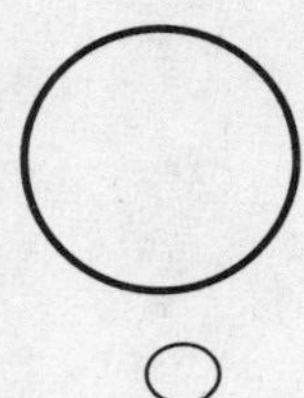

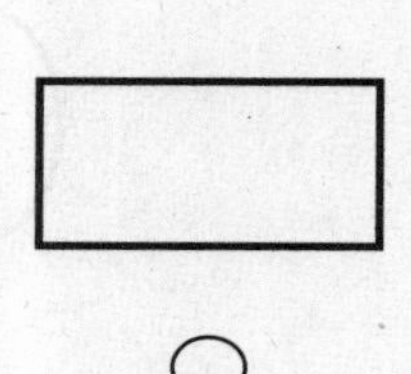

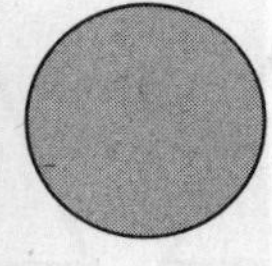
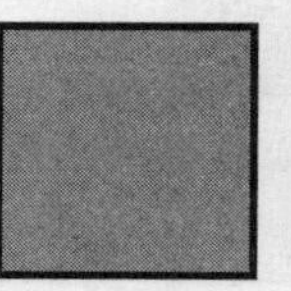

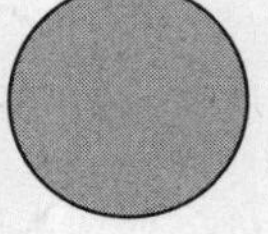

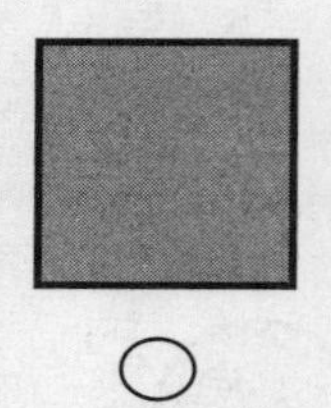
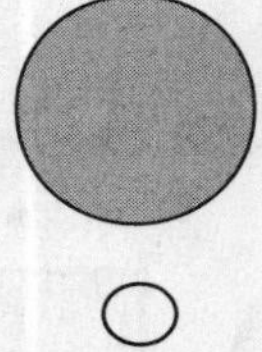
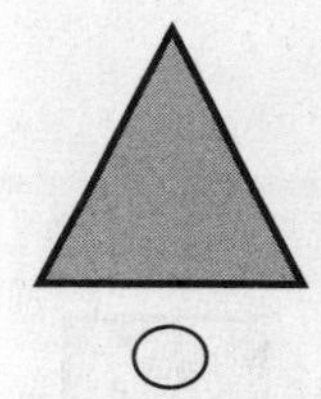

Directions:
3–5. Look at the pattern. Which shape comes next?

Chapter 10

Performance Assessment

CHILD'S TASK: Students choose appropriate color counters or connecting cubes to extend patterns.

Teacher Preparation/Instructions

In preparation for the assessment, do the following:

- Place four mats on a table. On each of the mats, place color counters or connecting cubes in the following patterns:

  Mat 1: AB Pattern—green, blue, green, blue, green, blue

  Mat 2: AAB Pattern—red, red, yellow, red, red, yellow

  Mat 3: ABB Pattern—orange, purple, purple, orange, purple, purple

  Mat 4: ABC Pattern—yellow green red yellow green red
- Provide counters for students to extend the patterns.

ONE WAY:

Tell students that they will use colored counters or connecting cubes to extend a variety of patterns.

1. Direct attention to Mat 1 (AB Pattern). Say: "Look at the pattern. Place the counter that comes next in the pattern."
2. Direct attention to Mat 2 (AAB Pattern). Say: "Look at the pattern. Place the counter that comes next in the pattern."
3. Direct attention to Mat 3 (ABB Pattern). Say "Look at the pattern. Place two counters that come next in the pattern."
4. Direct attention to Mat 4 (ABC Pattern). Say: "Look at the pattern. Place three counters that come next in the pattern."

ANOTHER WAY:

Have students use two-colored counters or connecting cubes to create an AB pattern on a mat. Then have them use the counters or cubes to create an AAB pattern. Next have them create an ABB pattern. Finally have students use three colored counters or connecting cubes to create an ABC pattern.

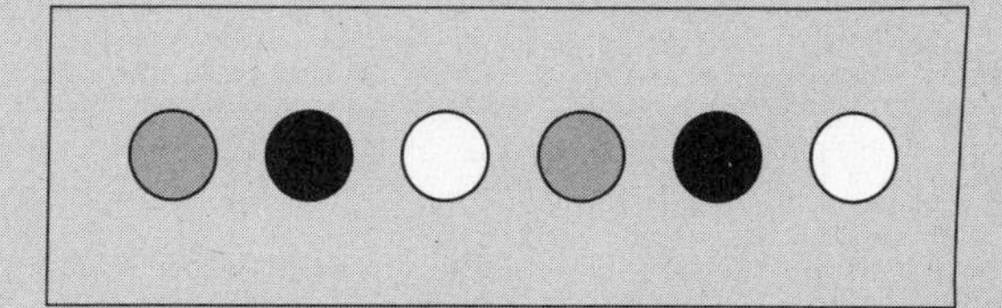

Chapter 10

Chapter 10

Performance Assessment Teacher's Notes

Target Skills

Recognize and extend a variety of patterns—AB, AAB, ABB, and ABC.

Task Description

Students choose appropriate color counters to extend patterns.

Teacher Notes

- Stress that students need to look at the colors already on the mat before they extend the pattern.
- During this exercise, ensure that students understand that they are to add only one counter each to Mat 1 and Mat 2, two counters to Mat 3, and three counters to Mat 4.

Scoring Rubric	
Score	Explanation
3	Students demonstrate an efficient strategy that enables them to solve the problem completely. Students will: • correctly identify and extend an AB pattern. • correctly identify and extend an AAB pattern. • correctly identify and extend an ABB pattern. • correctly identify and extend an ABC pattern.
2	Students demonstrate a strategy that enables them to solve the problem correctly. The strategy is disorganized or less efficient. Students may: • at first place a variety of counters on the mat but later recognize and correctly extend most of the patterns.
1	Children demonstrate a confused strategy that leads to difficulty in solving the problem. Most answers are incorrect, but students demonstrate knowledge of at least one concept. Students may: • be unable to extend most of the patterns but able to extend at least one pattern.

Name

Section Test (Chapters 8–10)

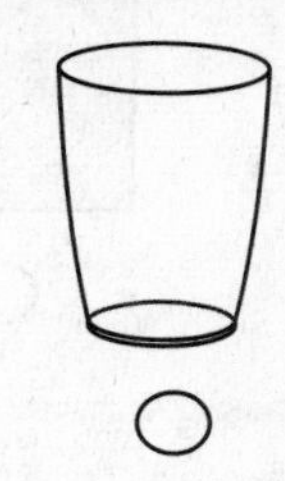

3

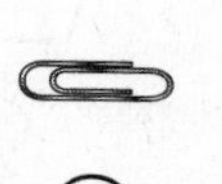

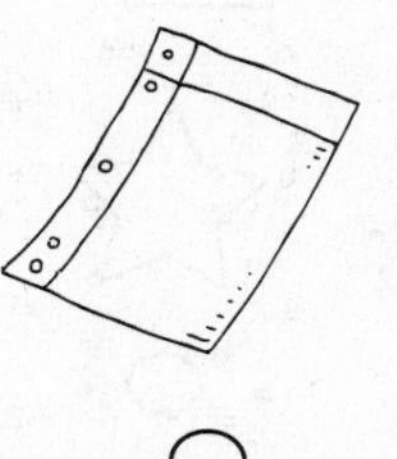

Name

Section Test (Chapters 8–10)

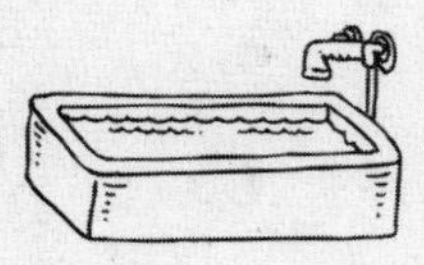
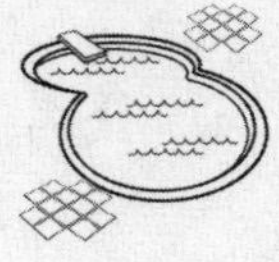
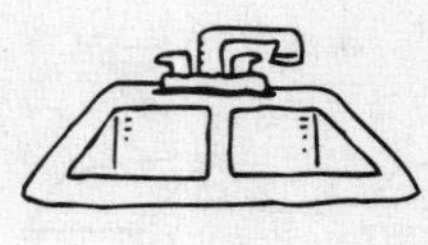

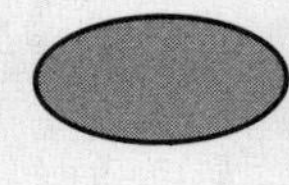

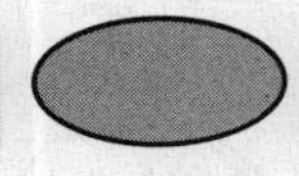
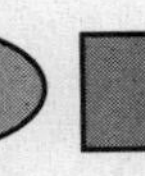
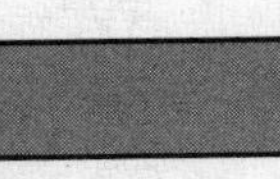
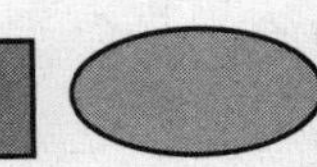
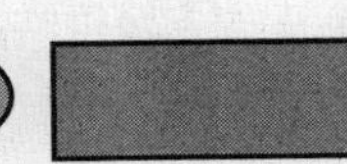

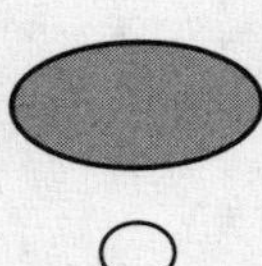
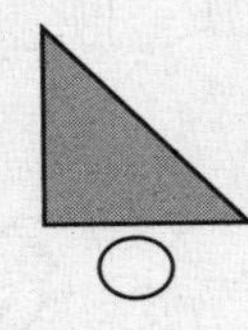
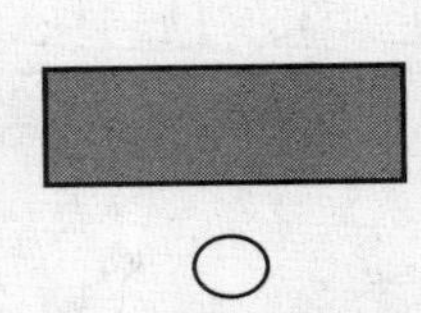

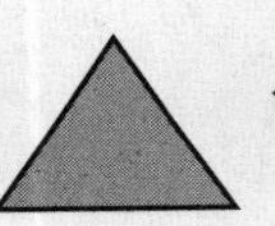
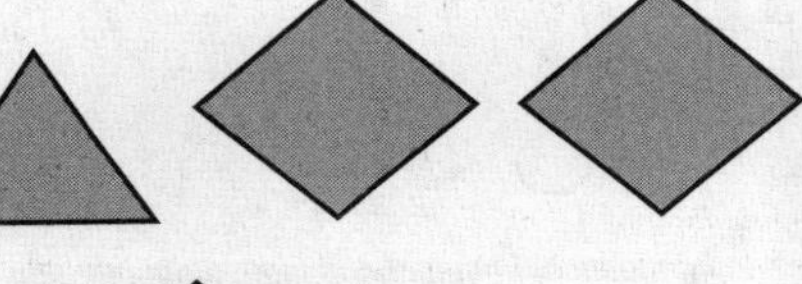

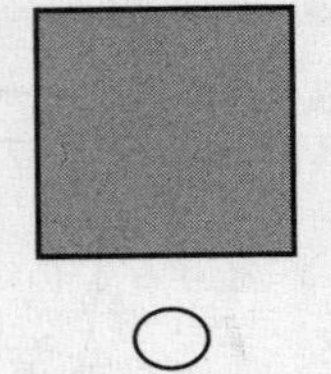
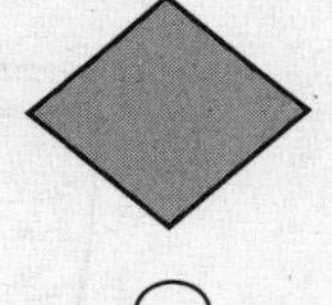
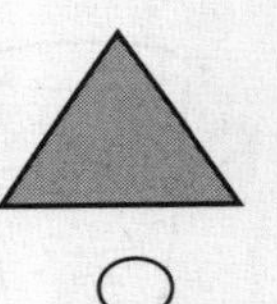

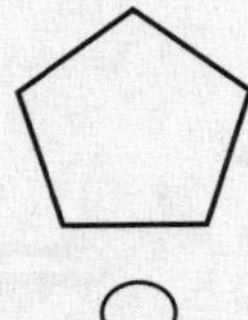
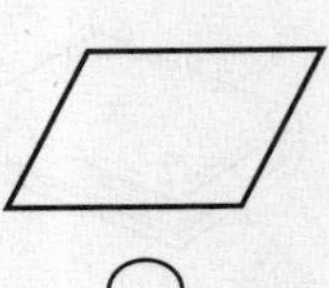

Section Test (Chapters 8–10)

Scoring Guide and Diagnostic Chart

Students missing Exercise . . .	Have trouble with . . .	Should review . . .
1	Equal or Unequal	Chapter 8, Lesson 2
2	Full or Empty	Chapter 8, Lesson 7
3	Heavy or Heavier	Chapter 9, Lesson 4
4	More and Most	Chapter 9, Lesson 6
5	AB Patterns	Chapter 10, Lesson 2
6	AAB Patterns	Chapter 10, Lesson 3
7	Identify and Extend Patterns	Chapter 10, Lesson 6

Teacher Directions

Read the following directions to students before they begin. Then, read each question followed by a pause to allow students time to work and choose an answer.

- **Write your name at the top of the page.**
- **I am going to read each question to you. Listen carefully before you choose an answer.**

1. Which shows the same number of chickens and barns?
2. Which glass is empty?
3. Which object is heavier than the chalk?

- **Turn the page over.**

4. Look at the objects. Which holds the most?
5. Look at the pattern. Which figure comes next in the pattern?
6. Look at the pattern. Which figure comes next?
7. Look at the pattern. Which figure comes next?

Section Test

Grade K

Name ____________________ Date ____________

Diagnostic and Placement Test

For each part, mark the box under the number of correctly answered questions.

Numbers, Operations, and Quantitative Reasoning (1–3)

Patterns, Relationships, and Algebraic Reasoning (4–6)

Geometry and Spatial Reasoning (7–11)

Measurement (12–13)

Probability and Statistics (14–15)

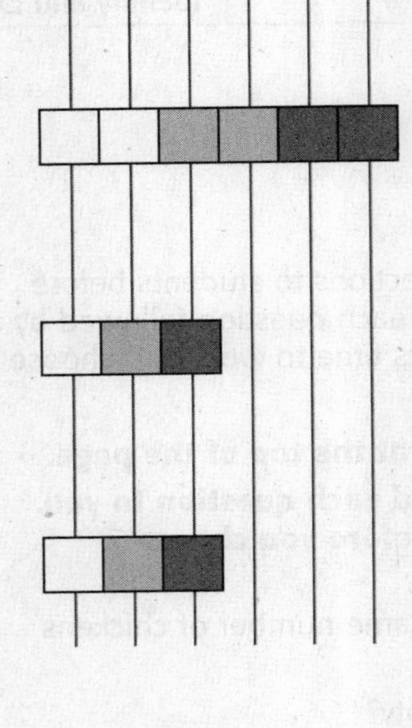

Mark the total number correct below.

Total

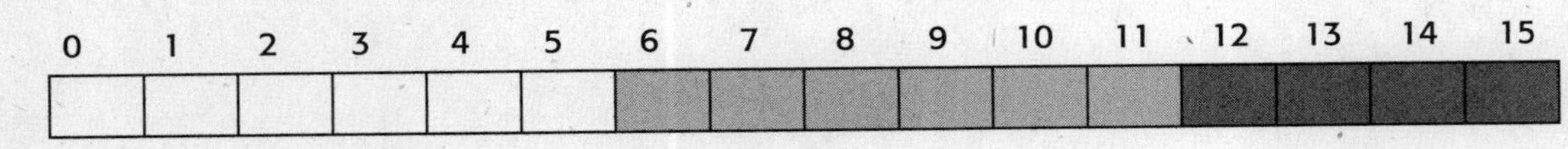

Key: Consider this student for…

- *Math Triumphs, Grade K*
- *Grade K Strategic Intervention*
- *Math Connects, Grade K*

Grade K

Name ______________________ Date ____________

Diagnostic and Placement Test

In the column on the left, mark the questions that the student answered *incorrectly*.

Strand	Question Number	Objective
Numbers, Operations and Quantitative Reasoning	☐ 1	Count with understanding and recognize how many in sets of objects.
	☐ 2	Count with understanding and recognize how many in sets of objects.
	☐ 3	Understand meanings of operations and how they relate to each other.
Patterns, Relationships and Algebraic Reasoning	☐ 4	Sort, classify, and order objects by size, number, and other properties.
	☐ 5	Recognize, describe, and extend patterns such as sequences of sounds and shapes or simple numeric patterns and translate from one representation to another.
	☐ 6	Analyze how both repeating and growing patterns are generated.
Geometry and Spatial Reasoning	☐ 7	Recognize, name, build, draw, compare, and sort two- and three-dimensional shapes.
	☐ 8	Describe attributes and parts of two-and three-dimensional shapes.
	☐ 9	Describe, name, and interpret relative positions in space and apply ideas about relative position.
	☐ 10	Find and name locations with simple relationships such as near to and in.
	☐ 11	Recognize geometric shapes and structures in the environment and specify their location such as, above, below, next to.
Measurement	☐ 12	Recognize the attributes of length, volume, weight, and area.
	☐ 13	Compare and order objects according to the attributes of length, volume, weight, and area.
Probability and Statistics	☐ 14	Sort and classify objects according to their attributes and organize data about the objects.
	☐ 15	Sort and classify objects according to their attributes and organize data about the objects.

Name ______________________ Date __________

Diagnostic and Placement Test

Student Performance Level	Number of Questions Correct	Suggestions for Intervention and Remediation
Intensive Intervention	**0–5**	Use *Math Triumphs* to accelerate the achievement of students who are significantly below grade level. Students should follow a personalized remediation plan. A variety of materials and instructional methods are recommended. For example, instruction and practice should be provided in print, technology, and hands-on lessons.
Strategic Intervention	**6–11**	Use additional Intervention and Remediation materials listed on the next page. This list of materials can provide helpful resources for students who struggle in the traditional mathematics program. Strategic intervention allows students to continue to remain in the *Math Connects* program, while receiving the differentiated instruction that they need. Teaching Tips and other resources may also be listed in the Teacher Edition.
Kindergarten	**12 or more**	Use *Math Connects*. This student does not require overall intervention. However, based on the student's performance on the different sections, intervention may be required. For example, a student who missed 2 or more questions in the Geometry and Spatial Reasoning section may require extra assistance as you cover these skills throughout the year.

A Special Note About Intervention

When using diagnostic tests, teachers should always question the reason behind the students' scores. Students can struggle with mathematics concepts for a variety of reasons. Personalized instruction is recommended for English language learners, students with specific learning disabilities, students with certain medical conditions, or for those who struggle with traditional instructional practice. Teachers should always consider the needs of the individual student when determining the best approach for instruction and program placement.

Grade K

Name ______________________ Date ____________

Diagnostic and Placement Test

This test contains 15 questions. Work each problem in the space on this page. Select the best answer. Write the answer as directed.

1 Count the apples. Write the number. __________

2 Put an X on the set of four cherries.

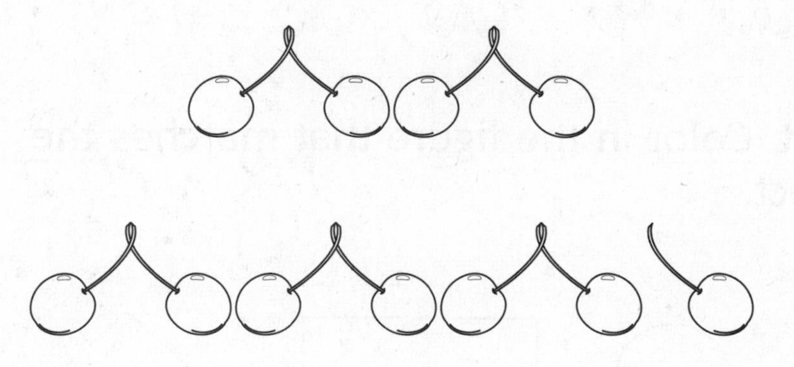

3 Circle the problem that fits the story.

$$\begin{array}{r} 2 \\ -\ 1 \\ \hline 1 \end{array} \qquad \begin{array}{r} 2 \\ +\ 1 \\ \hline 3 \end{array}$$

4 Look at the first square. Circle the squares that are the same size.

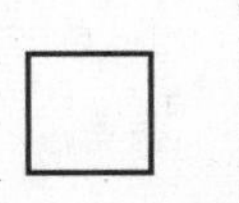 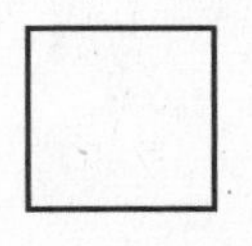 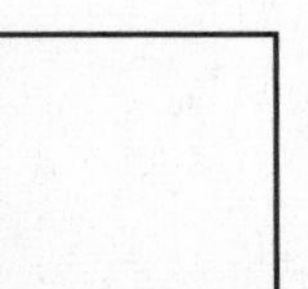 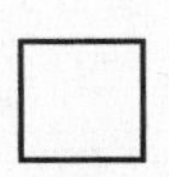 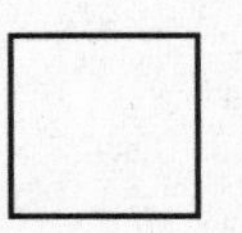 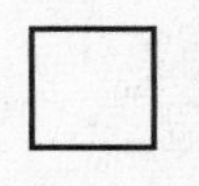

GK Placement Test

5 Circle the shape that comes next.

6 Look at the pattern. Circle the part that repeats.

7 Look at the object. Color in the figure that matches the shape of the object.

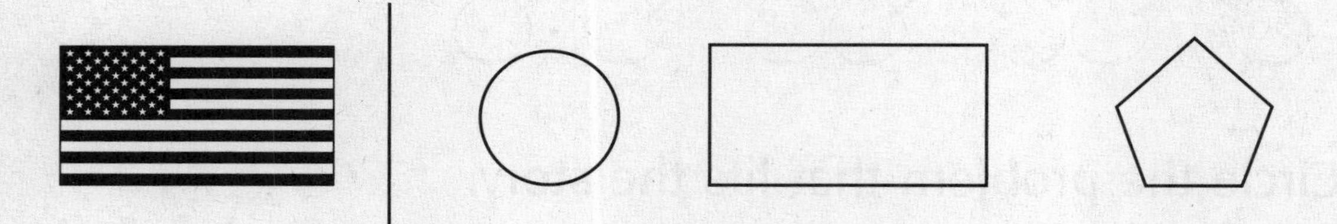

8 Put an X on the objects that can stack.

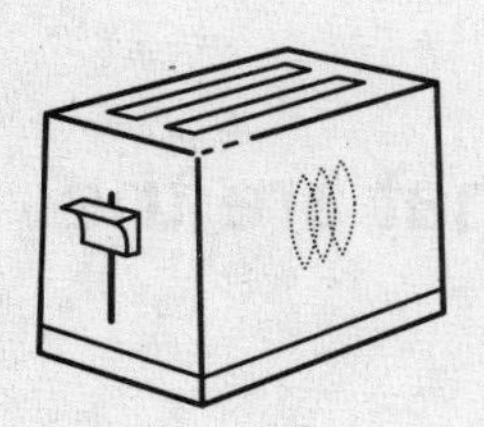 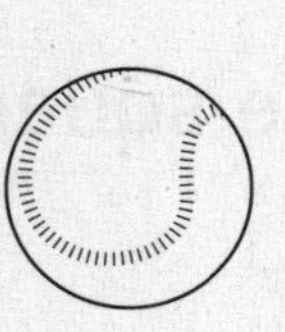 

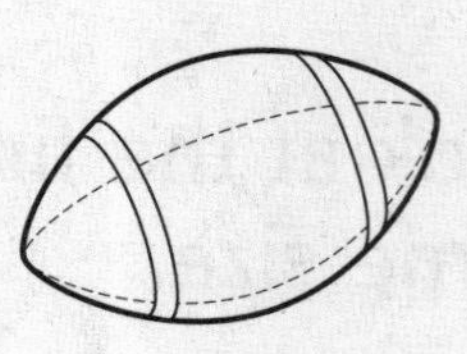

9 Put an X on the sailboat that is in the middle.

10 Put an X on the crayon that is under the table.

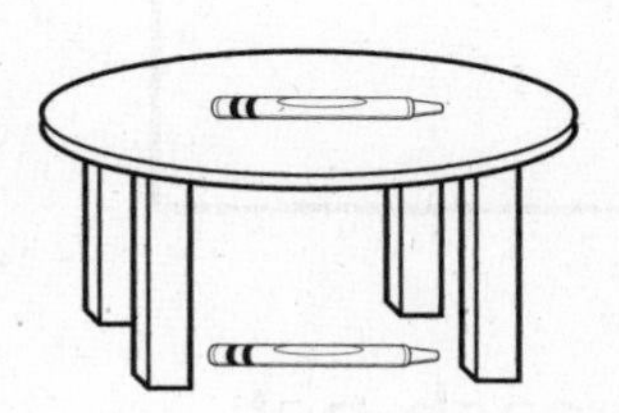

11 Put an X on the object that is next to the tree.

12 Circle the shorter object.

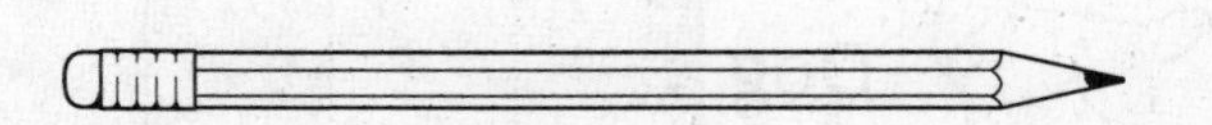

13 Circle the object that holds more.

GK Placement Test

14 Sort the crayons by color. Use tally marks to show how many crayons are in each group.

Number of Crayons	
Crayons	Tally
crayon	

15 Look at the group. Write how many of each pet.

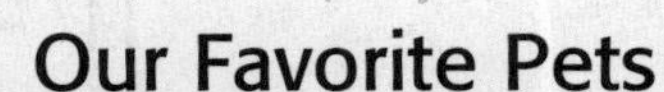

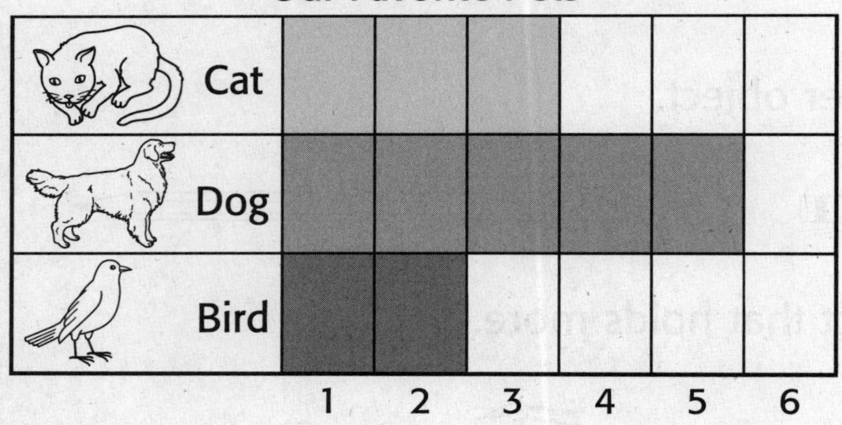

______  ______  ______ 

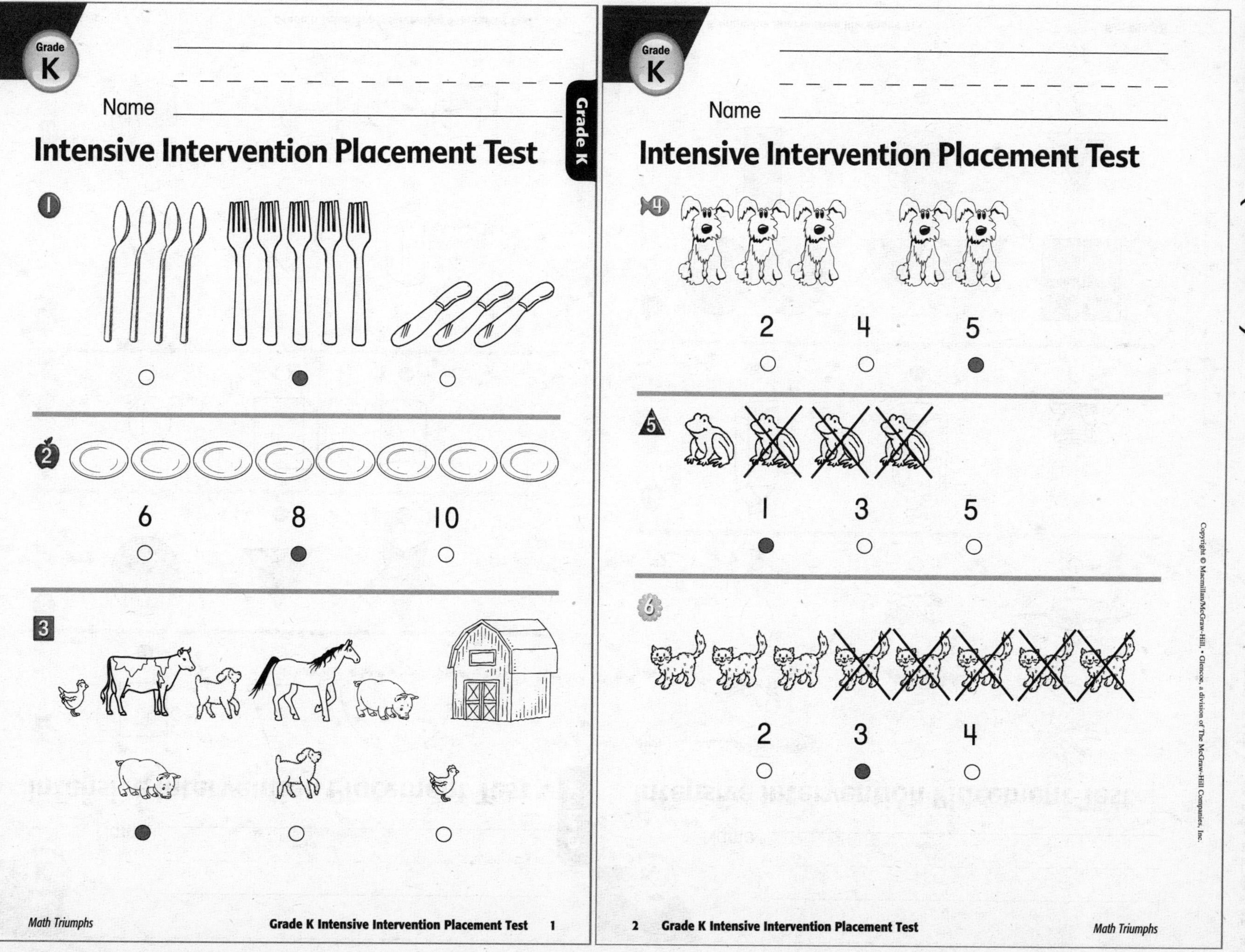

Grade K

Name

Intensive Intervention Placement Test

Grade K

1

2

6 8 10

3

Grade K

Name

Intensive Intervention Placement Test

4

2 4 5

5

1 3 5

6

2 3 4

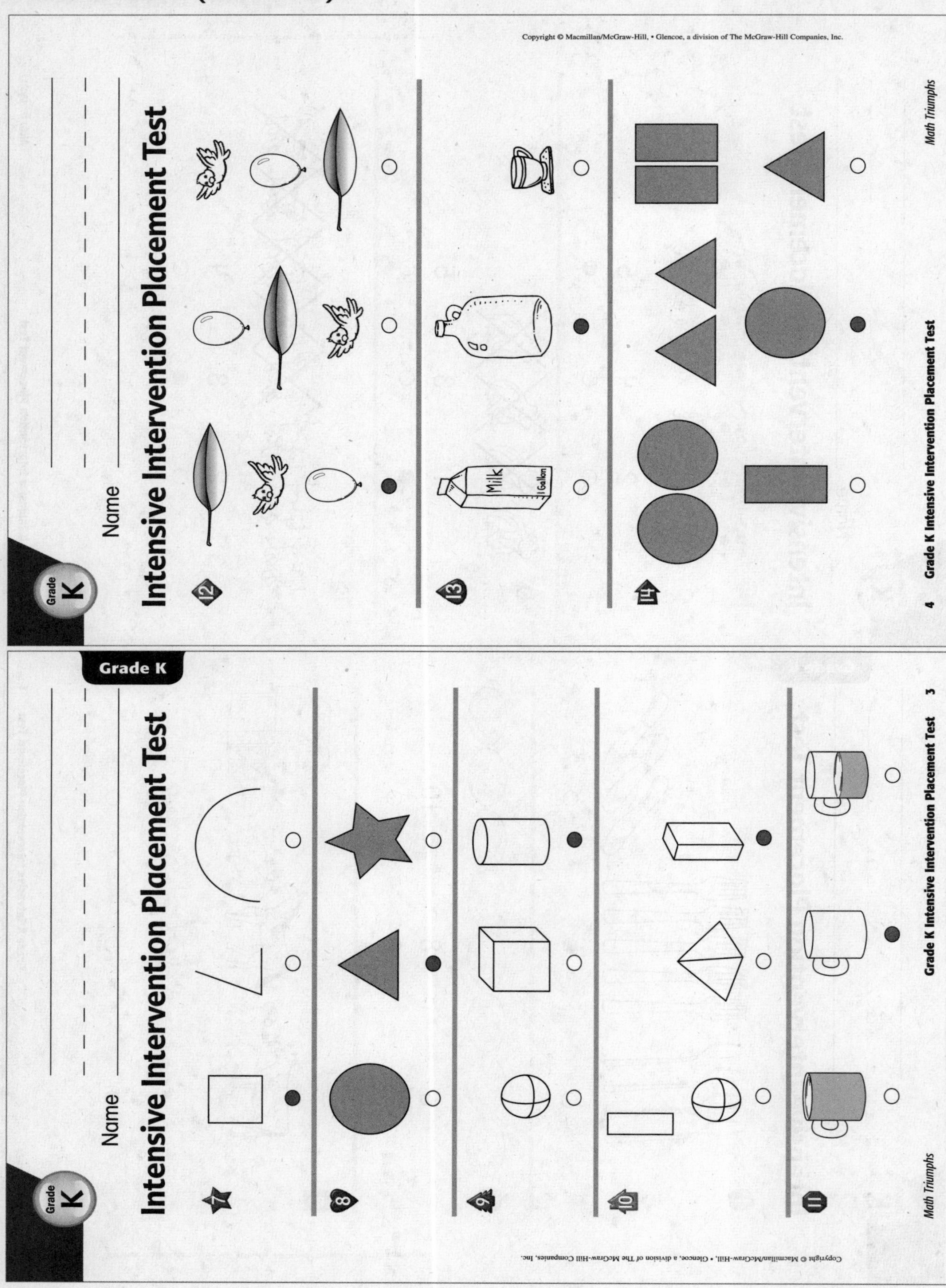
Grade K
Name
Intensive Intervention Placement Test
Milk
1 Gallon
4 Grade K Intensive Intervention Placement Test
Math Triumphs
Grade K Intensive Intervention Placement Test 3
Copyright © Macmillan/McGraw-Hill, • Glencoe, a division of The McGraw-Hill Companies, Inc.

Answers (Grade K)

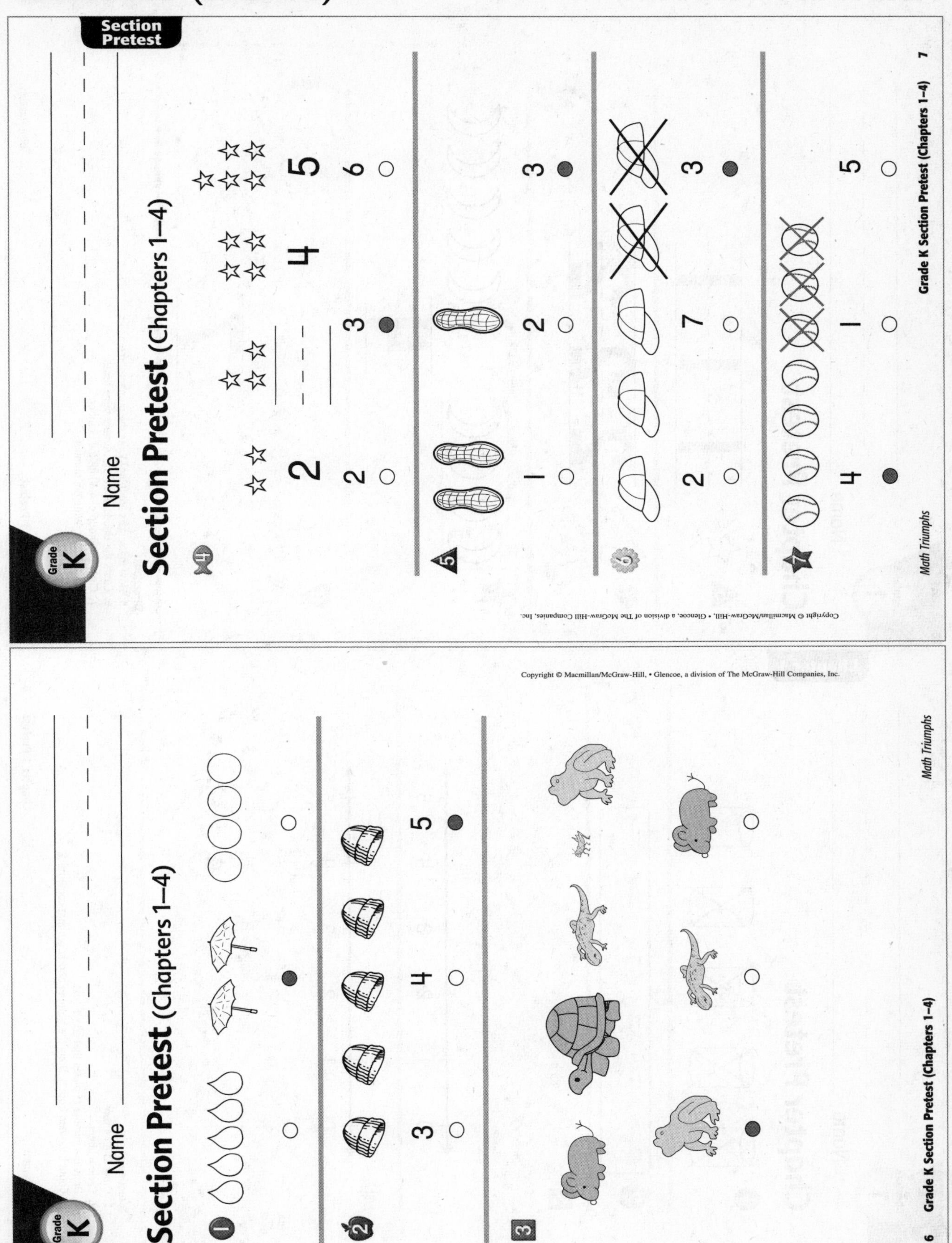

Grade K

Name

Section Pretest (Chapters 1–4)

1

2

3 4 5

3

Section Pretest

Grade K

Name

Section Pretest (Chapters 1–4)

4

2 4 5

2 3 6

5

1 2 3

6

2 7 3

7

4 1 5

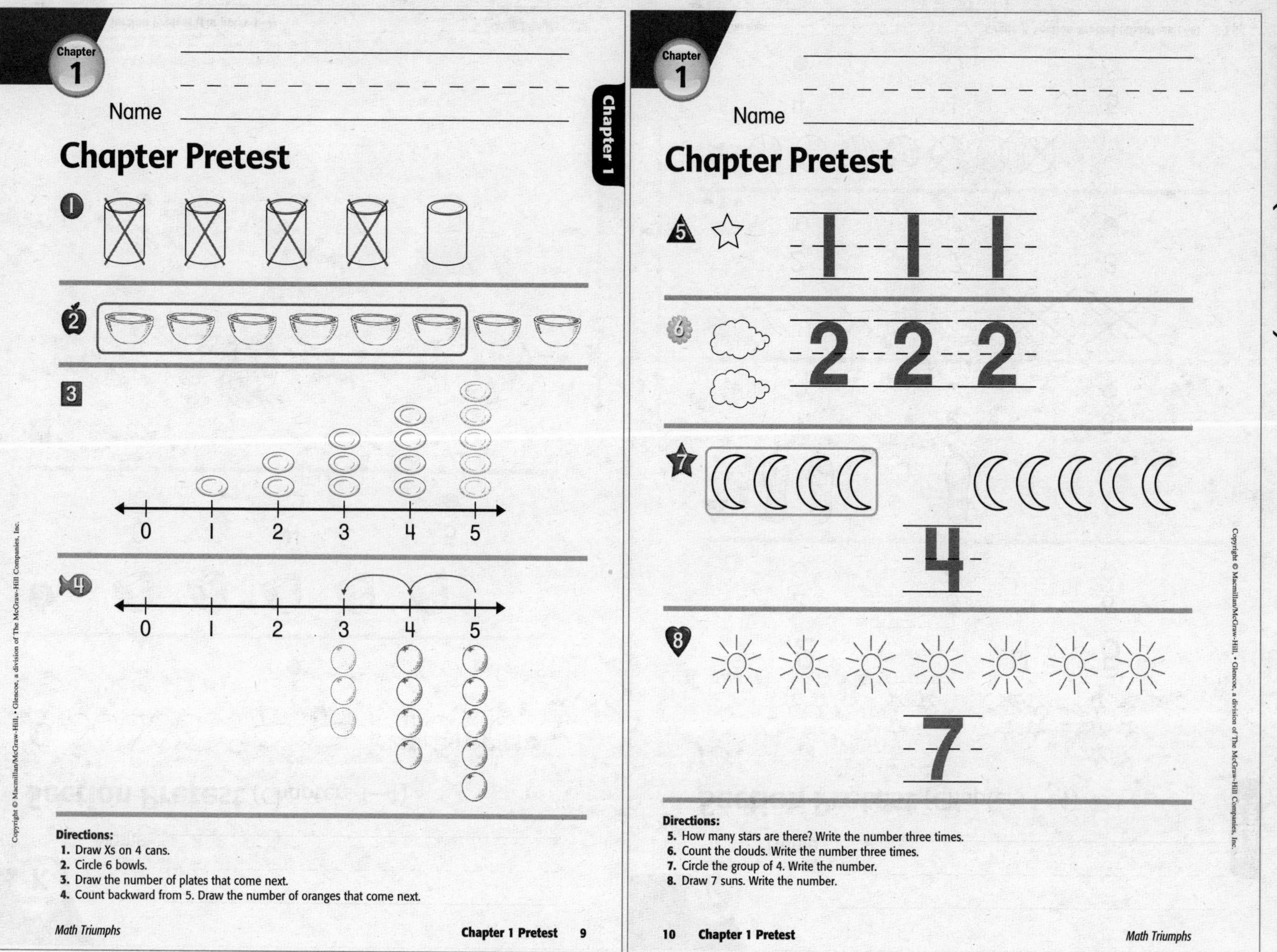

Chapter 1

Chapter Pretest

Name ______________

1.

2.

3. 0 1 2 3 4 5

4. 0 1 2 3 4 5

Directions:
1. Draw Xs on 4 cans.
2. Circle 6 bowls.
3. Draw the number of plates that come next.
4. Count backward from 5. Draw the number of oranges that come next.

Math Triumphs — Chapter 1 Pretest 9

Chapter 1

Chapter Pretest

Name ______________

5. 1 1 1

6. 2 2 2

7. 4

8. 7

Directions:
5. How many stars are there? Write the number three times.
6. Count the clouds. Write the number three times.
7. Circle the group of 4. Write the number.
8. Draw 7 suns. Write the number.

10 Chapter 1 Pretest — *Math Triumphs*

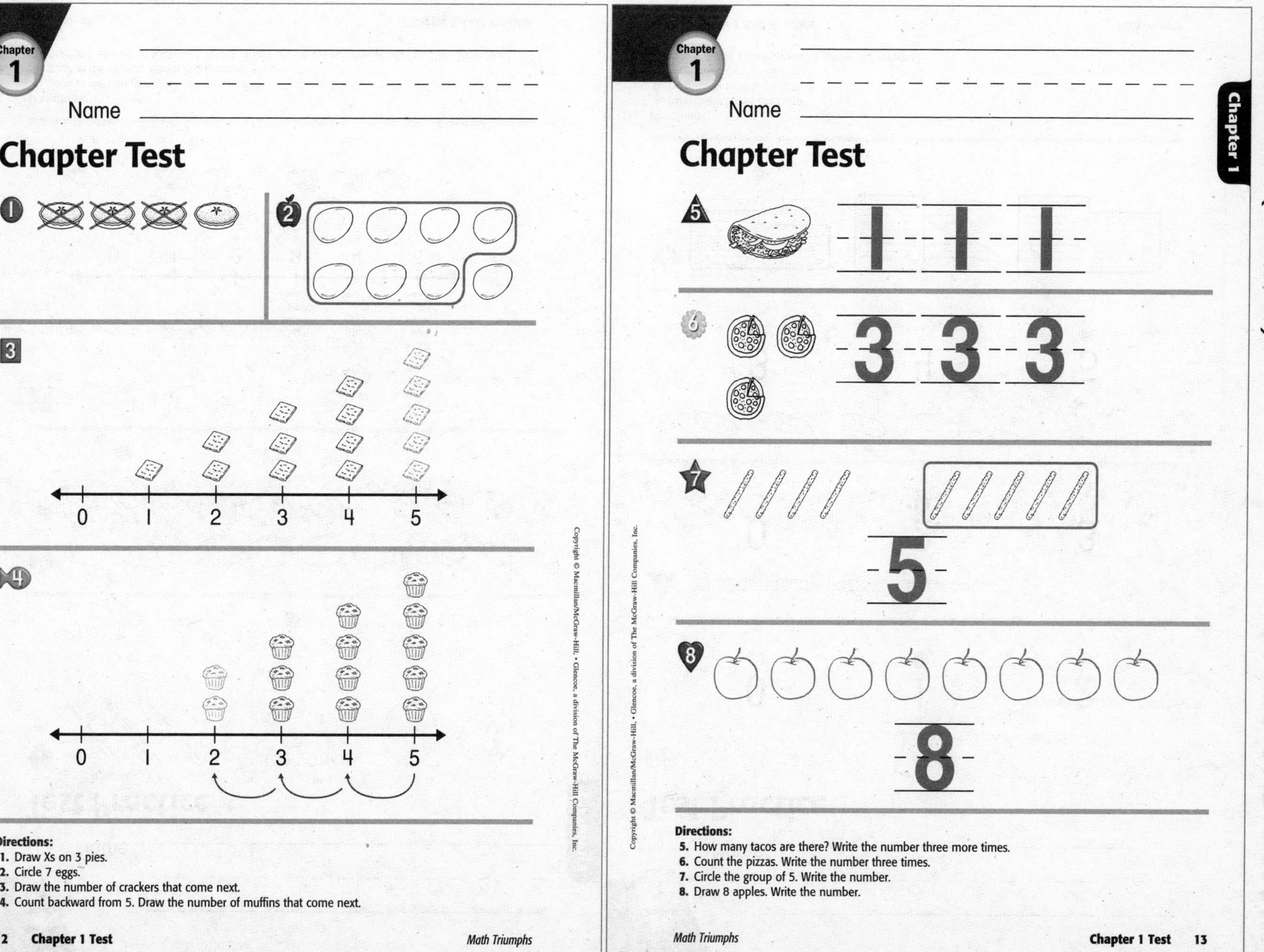

Chapter 1

Name

Chapter Test

1

2

3

0 1 2 3 4 5

4

0 1 2 3 4 5

Directions:

1. Draw Xs on 3 pies.
2. Circle 7 eggs.
3. Draw the number of crackers that come next.
4. Count backward from 5. Draw the number of muffins that come next.

12 Chapter 1 Test *Math Triumphs*

Copyright © Macmillan/McGraw-Hill, • Glencoe, a division of The McGraw-Hill Companies, Inc.

Chapter 1

Name

Chapter Test

5

1 1 1

6

3 3 3

7

5

8

8

Directions:

5. How many tacos are there? Write the number three more times.
6. Count the pizzas. Write the number three times.
7. Circle the group of 5. Write the number.
8. Draw 8 apples. Write the number.

Math Triumphs Chapter 1 Test 13

Copyright © Macmillan/McGraw-Hill, • Glencoe, a division of The McGraw-Hill Companies, Inc.

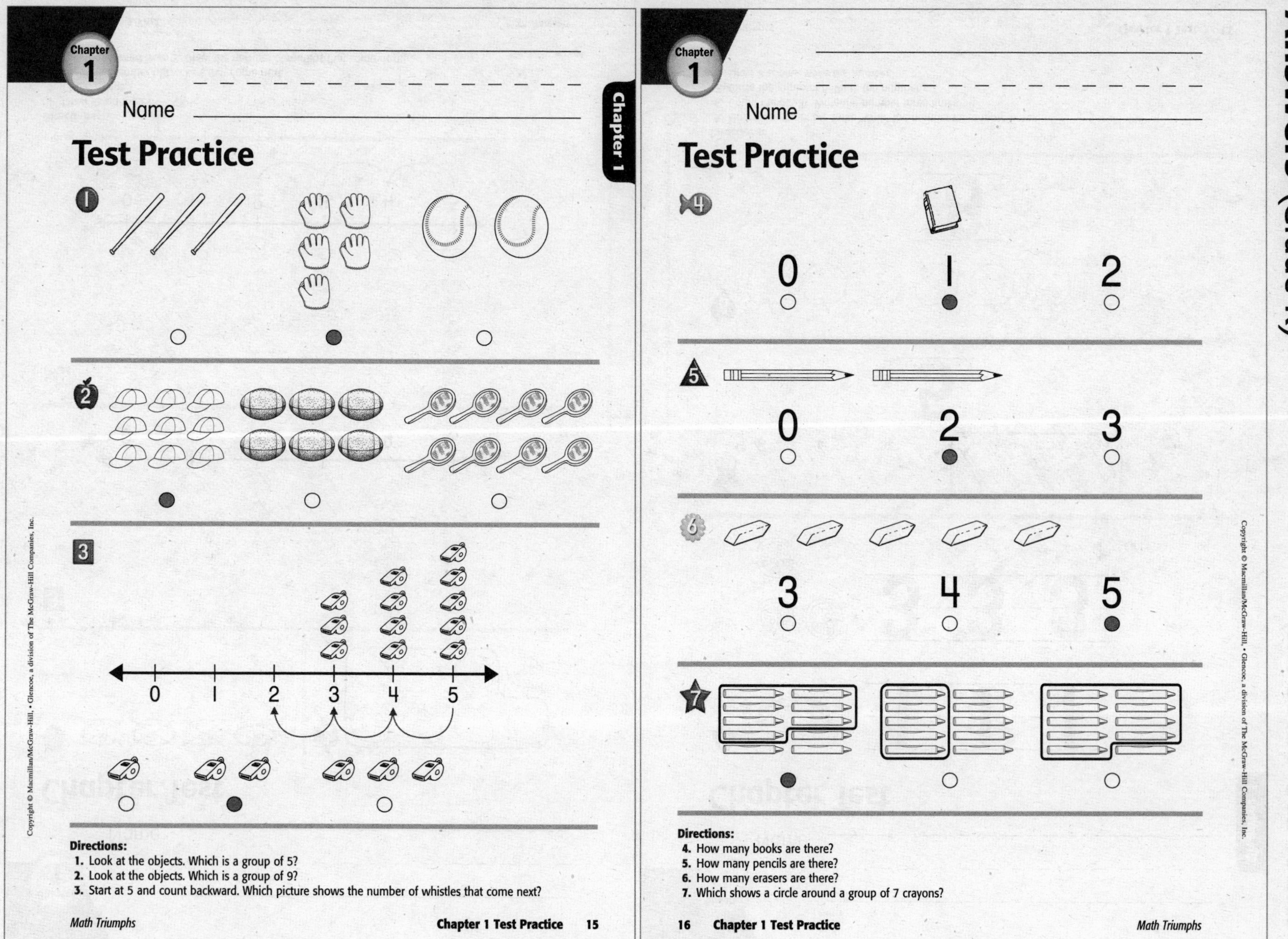

Chapter 1

Chapter 1

Test Practice

Name

1

2

3

0 1 2 3 4 5

Directions:
1. Look at the objects. Which is a group of 5?
2. Look at the objects. Which is a group of 9?
3. Start at 5 and count backward. Which picture shows the number of whistles that come next?

Math Triumphs **Chapter 1 Test Practice** 15

Chapter 1

Test Practice

Name

4

0 1 2

5

0 2 3

6

3 4 5

7

Directions:
4. How many books are there?
5. How many pencils are there?
6. How many erasers are there?
7. Which shows a circle around a group of 7 crayons?

16 **Chapter 1 Test Practice** *Math Triumphs*

Chapter 2

Name

Chapter Pretest

Chapter 2

1. 0 1 (2) 3 4 5

2.

3.

4.

5.

Directions:
1. Circle the number that comes just before 3.
2. Circle the duck that is last in line.
3. Circle the second bird.
4. Circle the fourth animal.
5. Circle the group with the same number of animals as the group of chickens.

Chapter 2

Name

Chapter Pretest

6.

7.  7 6 5 4 3

8.

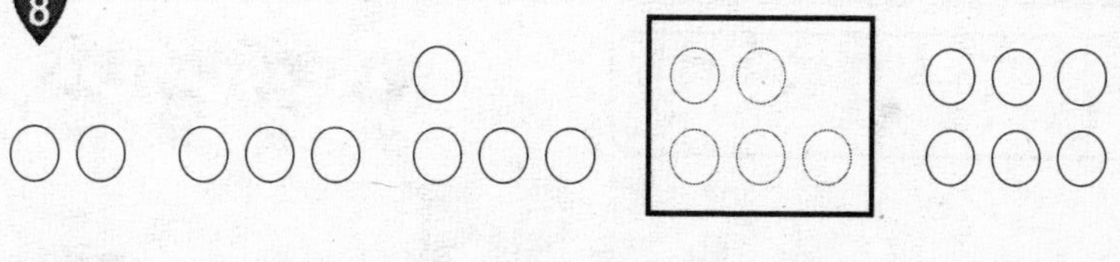

Directions:
6. Draw an X on the group that is less than the other.
7. Look for a pattern. Write the missing number.
8. Look for a pattern. Draw a picture in the box for the missing number.

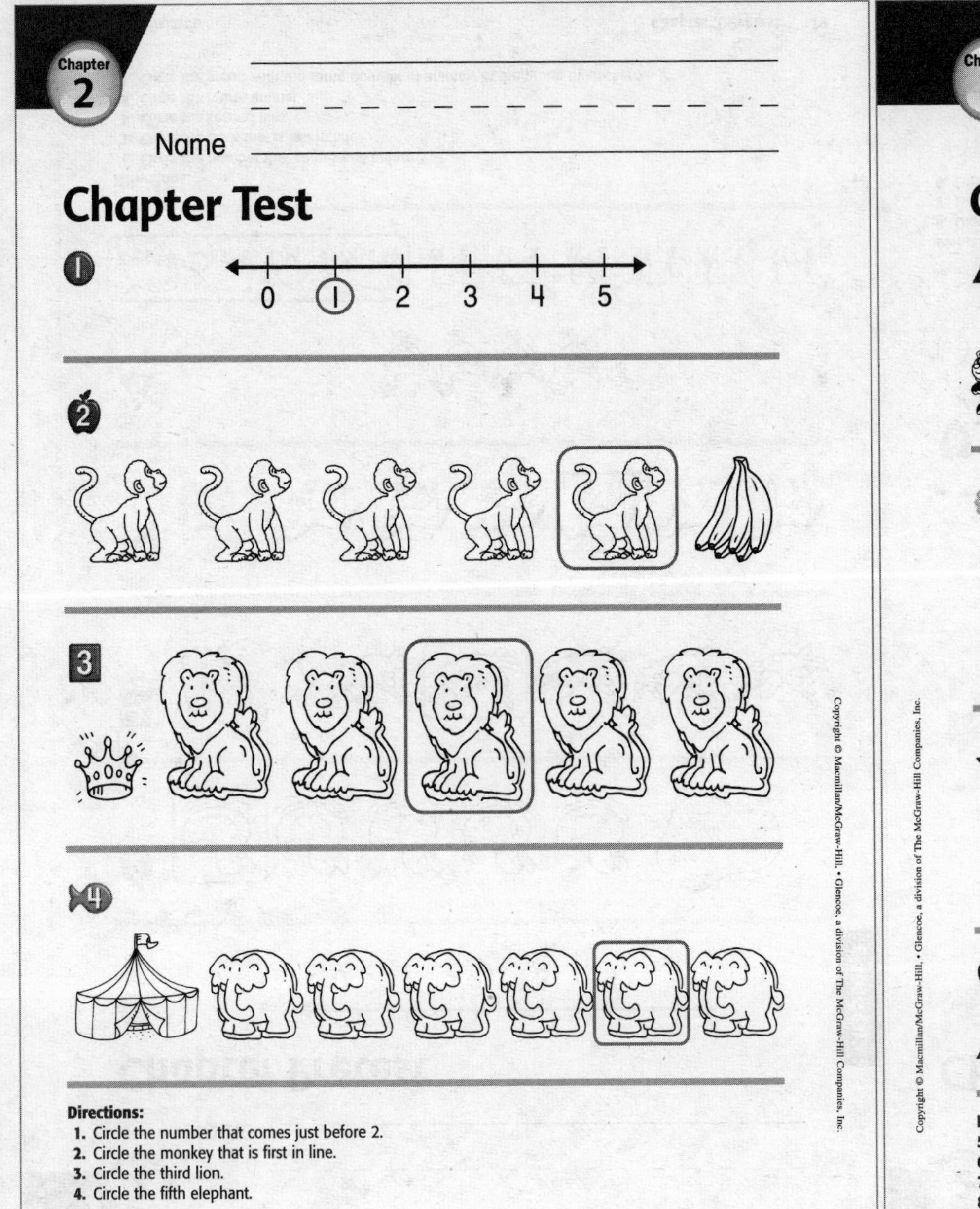

Chapter 2

Name

Chapter Test

1 0 ① 2 3 4 5

2

3

4

Directions:
1. Circle the number that comes just before 2.
2. Circle the monkey that is first in line.
3. Circle the third lion.
4. Circle the fifth elephant.

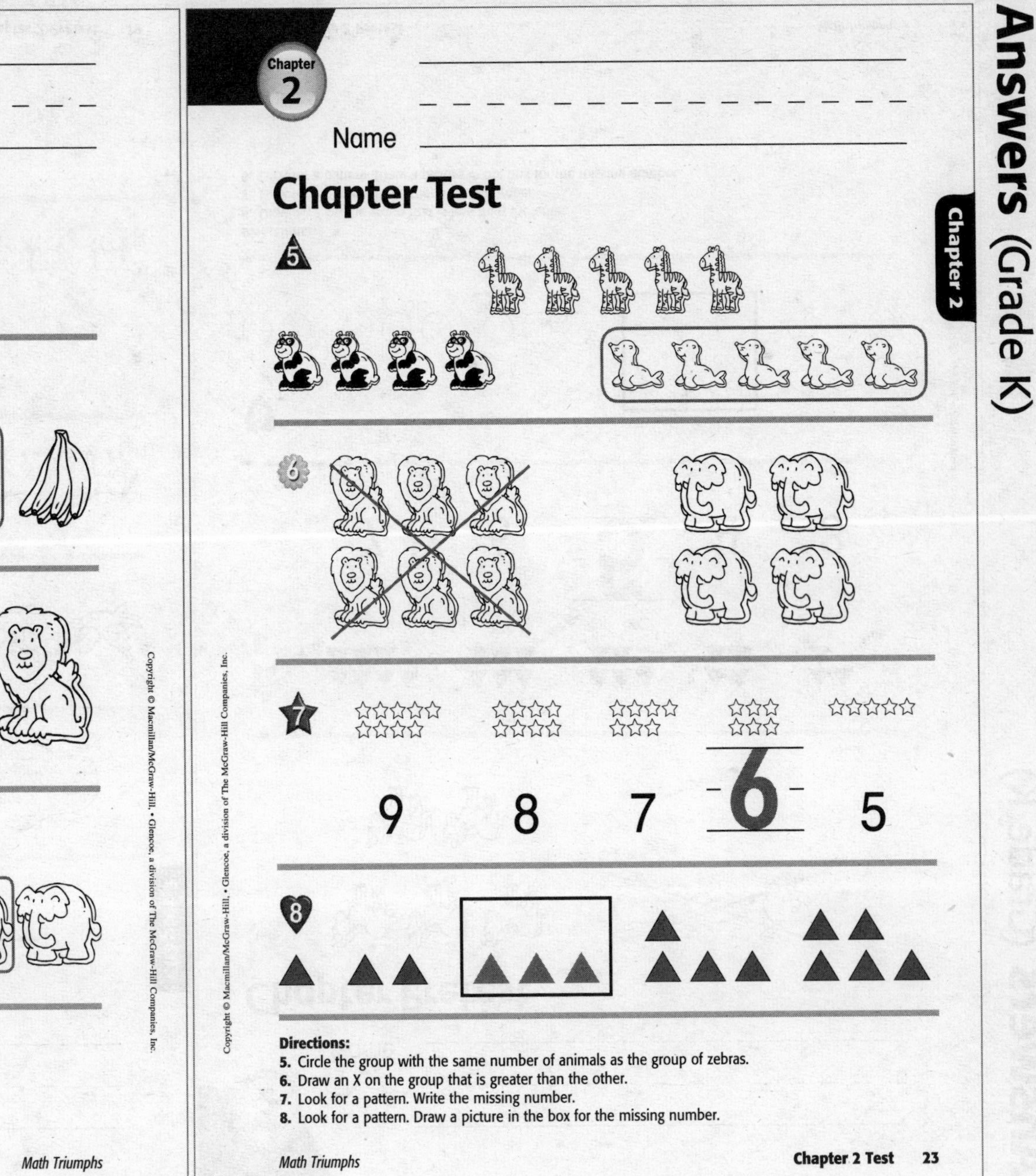

Chapter 2

Name

Chapter Test

5

6

7

9 8 7 6 5

8

Directions:
5. Circle the group with the same number of animals as the group of zebras.
6. Draw an X on the group that is greater than the other.
7. Look for a pattern. Write the missing number.
8. Look for a pattern. Draw a picture in the box for the missing number.

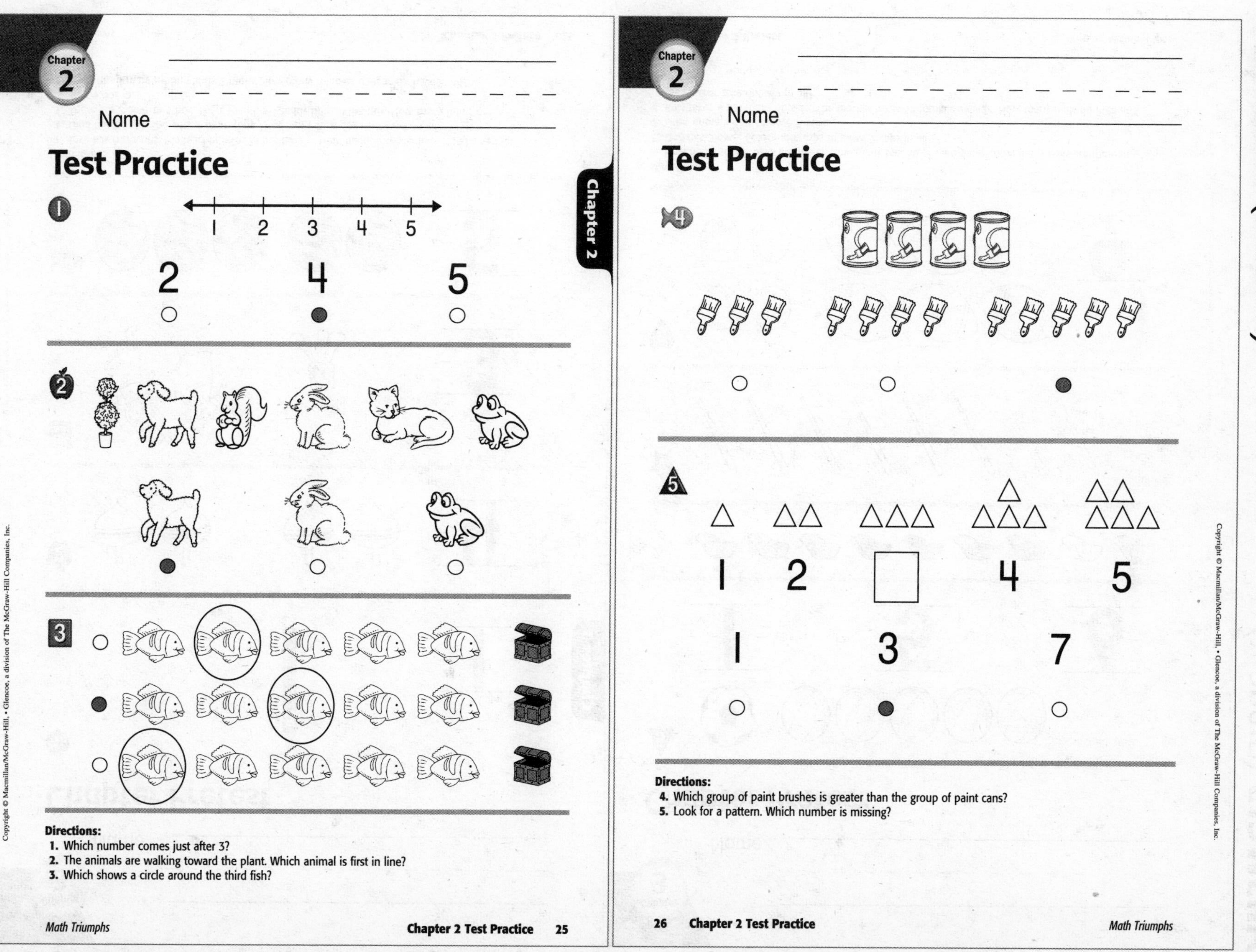

Chapter 2

Name

Test Practice

1

1 2 3 4 5

2 ○ 4 ● 5 ○

2

3

Directions:

1. Which number comes just after 3?
2. The animals are walking toward the plant. Which animal is first in line?
3. Which shows a circle around the third fish?

Math Triumphs — Chapter 2 Test Practice 25

Chapter 2

Name

Test Practice

4

○ ○ ●

5

1 2 □ 4 5

1 ○ 3 ● 7 ○

Directions:

4. Which group of paint brushes is greater than the group of paint cans?
5. Look for a pattern. Which number is missing?

26 Chapter 2 Test Practice — Math Triumphs

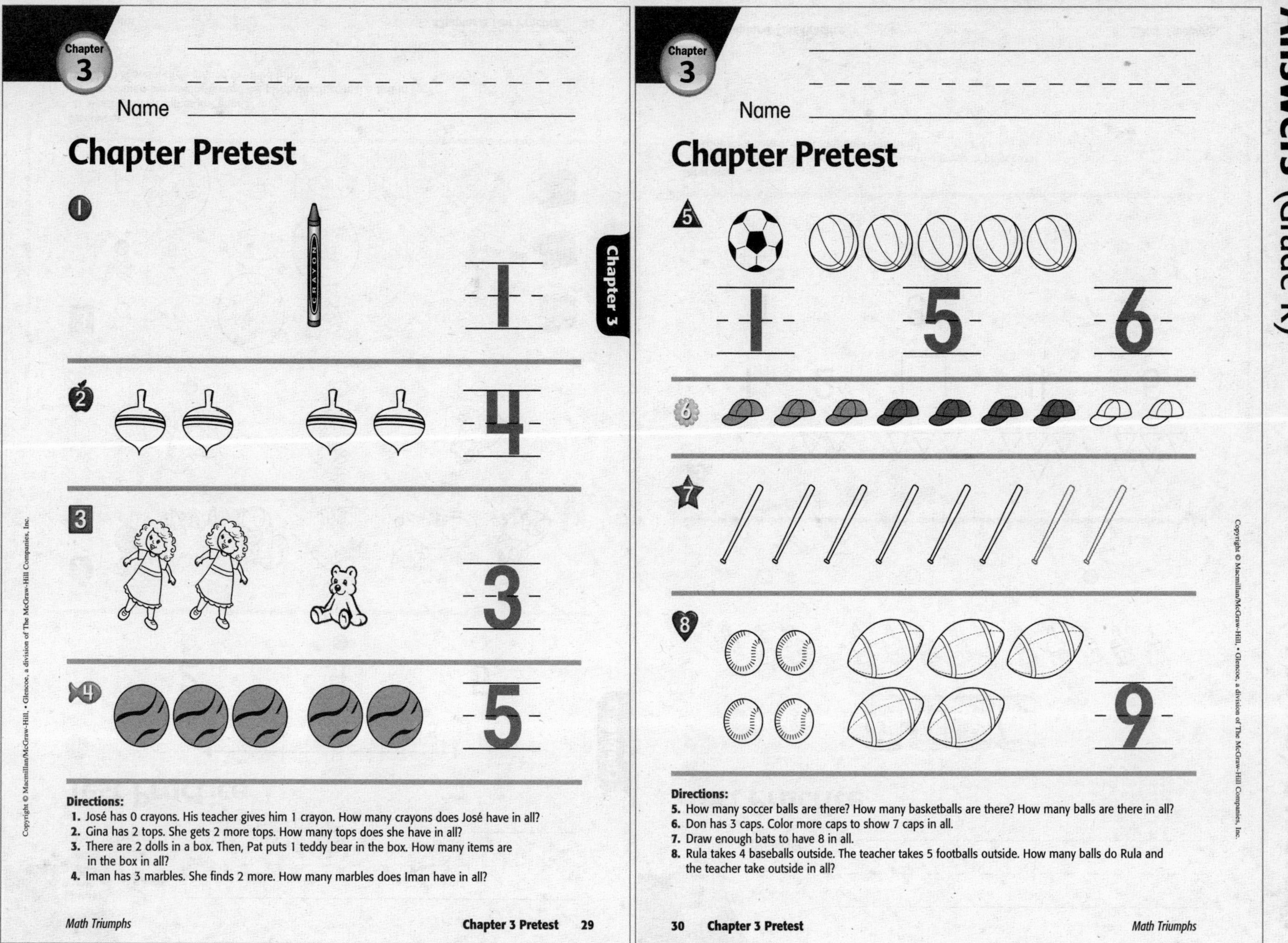

Chapter 3

Name

Chapter Pretest

1 — 1

2 — 4

3 — 3

4 — 5

Directions:

1. José has 0 crayons. His teacher gives him 1 crayon. How many crayons does José have in all?
2. Gina has 2 tops. She gets 2 more tops. How many tops does she have in all?
3. There are 2 dolls in a box. Then, Pat puts 1 teddy bear in the box. How many items are in the box in all?
4. Iman has 3 marbles. She finds 2 more. How many marbles does Iman have in all?

Math Triumphs **Chapter 3 Pretest** 29

Chapter 3

Name

Chapter Pretest

5 — 1, 5, 6

6

7

8 — 9

Directions:

5. How many soccer balls are there? How many basketballs are there? How many balls are there in all?
6. Don has 3 caps. Color more caps to show 7 caps in all.
7. Draw enough bats to have 8 in all.
8. Rula takes 4 baseballs outside. The teacher takes 5 footballs outside. How many balls do Rula and the teacher take outside in all?

30 **Chapter 3 Pretest** *Math Triumphs*

Chapter 3

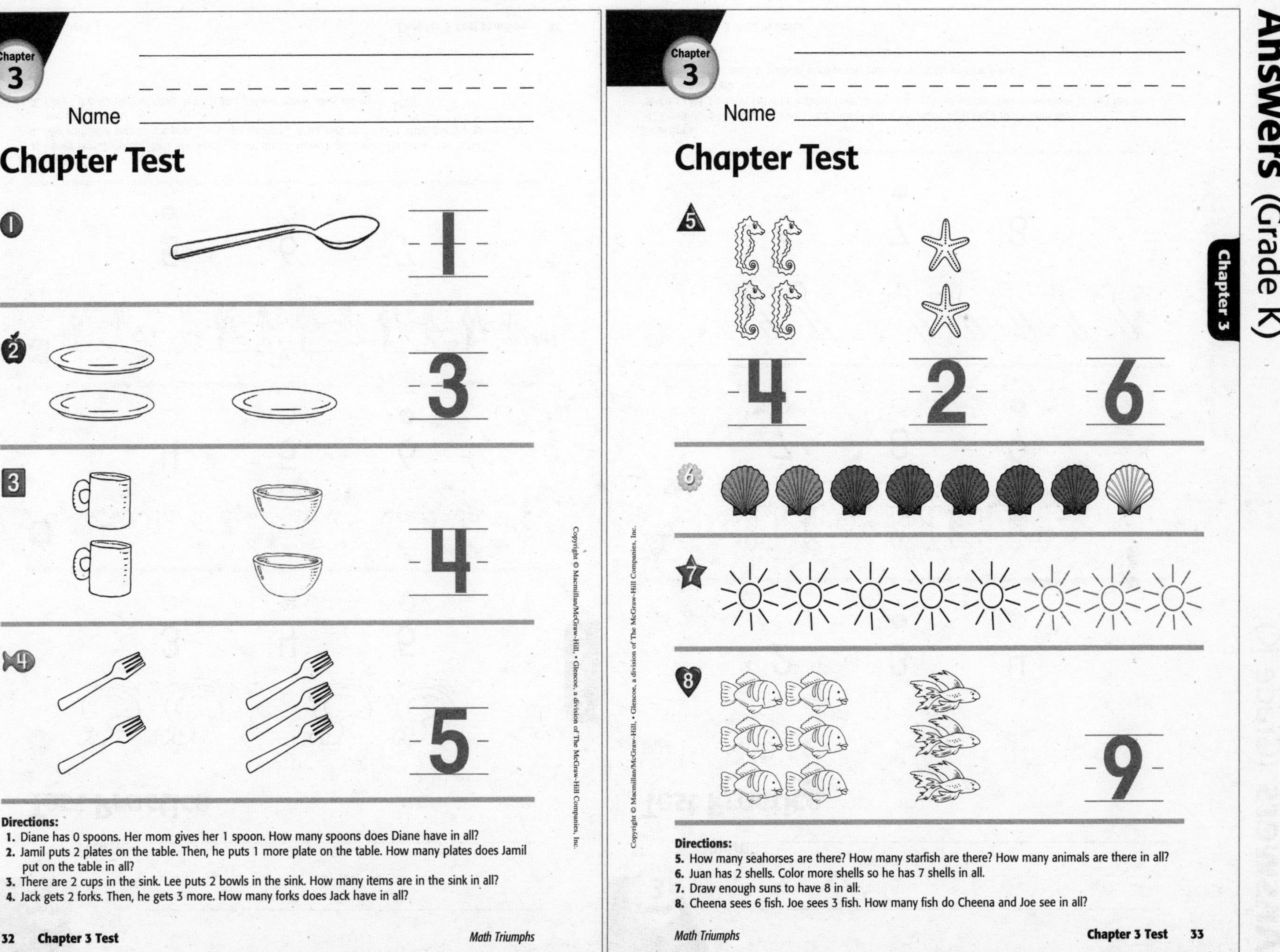

Chapter 3

Name ______

Chapter Test

1. 1
2. 3
3. 4
4. 5

Directions:
1. Diane has 0 spoons. Her mom gives her 1 spoon. How many spoons does Diane have in all?
2. Jamil puts 2 plates on the table. Then, he puts 1 more plate on the table. How many plates does Jamil put on the table in all?
3. There are 2 cups in the sink. Lee puts 2 bowls in the sink. How many items are in the sink in all?
4. Jack gets 2 forks. Then, he gets 3 more. How many forks does Jack have in all?

Chapter 3

Name ______

Chapter Test

5. 4 2 6
6.
7.
8. 9

Directions:
5. How many seahorses are there? How many starfish are there? How many animals are there in all?
6. Juan has 2 shells. Color more shells so he has 7 shells in all.
7. Draw enough suns to have 8 in all.
8. Cheena sees 6 fish. Joe sees 3 fish. How many fish do Cheena and Joe see in all?

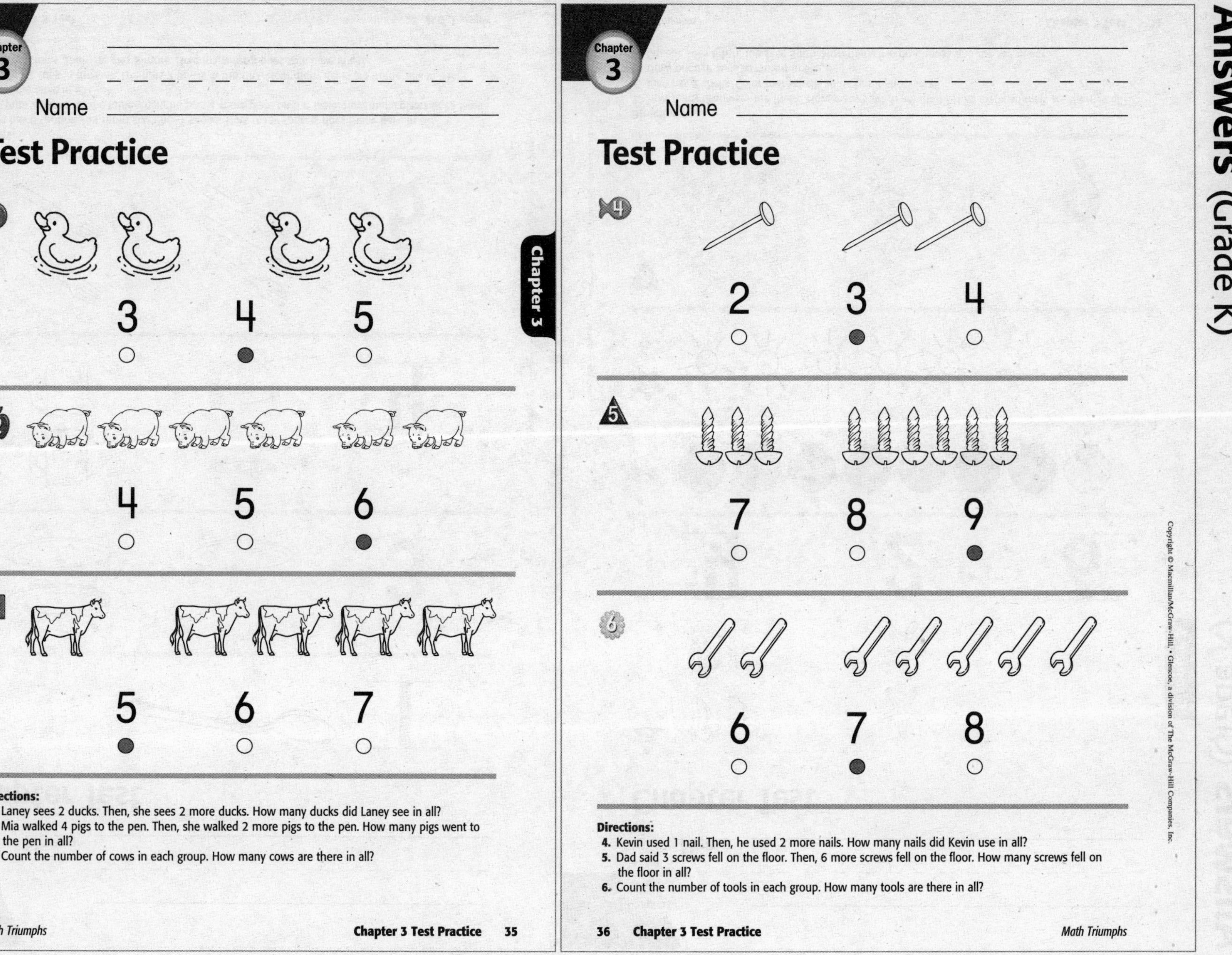

Chapter 3

Name

Test Practice

1. 3 ○ 4 ● 5 ○

2. 4 ○ 5 ○ 6 ●

3. 5 ● 6 ○ 7 ○

Directions:
1. Laney sees 2 ducks. Then, she sees 2 more ducks. How many ducks did Laney see in all?
2. Mia walked 4 pigs to the pen. Then, she walked 2 more pigs to the pen. How many pigs went to the pen in all?
3. Count the number of cows in each group. How many cows are there in all?

Math Triumphs Chapter 3 Test Practice 35

Chapter 3

Name

Test Practice

4. 2 ○ 3 ● 4 ○

5. 7 ○ 8 ○ 9 ●

6. 6 ○ 7 ● 8 ○

Directions:
4. Kevin used 1 nail. Then, he used 2 more nails. How many nails did Kevin use in all?
5. Dad said 3 screws fell on the floor. Then, 6 more screws fell on the floor. How many screws fell on the floor in all?
6. Count the number of tools in each group. How many tools are there in all?

36 Chapter 3 Test Practice *Math Triumphs*

Chapter 4

Name ______________________

Chapter Pretest

1. 1

2. 2

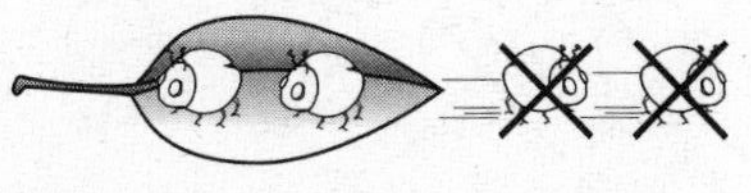

3. 4

4. 3

Directions:

1. There are 2 birds in the nest. Then, 1 bird flies away. How many birds are left?
2. There are 4 bugs on a leaf. Then, 2 crawl away. How many bugs are left?
3. Julio has 5 bones. He gives 1 bone to his dog. Draw an X on 1 bone. How many bones are left?
4. There are 6 dogs in the yard. Three dogs go into the house. Draw an X on 3 dogs. How many dogs are left in the yard?

Chapter 4

Chapter 4

Name ______________________

Chapter Pretest

5. 5

6. 7

7. 4

8. 0

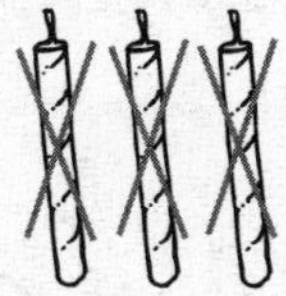

Directions:

5. A store has 7 lamps. A man buys 2 lamps. How many lamps are left?
6. A box has 8 lightbulbs. One lightbulb was taken out of the box. Draw an X on 1 lightbulb. How many lightbulbs are left in the box?
7. There are 9 flashlights on the table. Campers take 5 flashlights. Draw an X on 5 flashlights. How many flashlights are left on the table?
8. There are 3 candles in the kitchen. Dad takes 3 candles out of the kitchen. Draw an X on 3 candles. How many candles are left in the kitchen?

Chapter 4

Name ______________________

Chapter Test

1 — 0

2 — 1

3 — 3

4 — 2

Directions:

1. There are 2 mittens on the table. Then, 2 mittens blow away in the wind. How many mittens are left?
2. There are 4 caps in the closet. The children take 3 caps out of the closet. How many caps are left?
3. There are 5 shirts in the drawer. Isaac takes 2 shirts out of the drawer. Draw Xs on 2 shirts. How many shirts are left in the drawer?
4. There are 6 boots by the door. The dog runs away with 4 of the boots. Draw Xs on 4 boots. How many boots are left by the door?

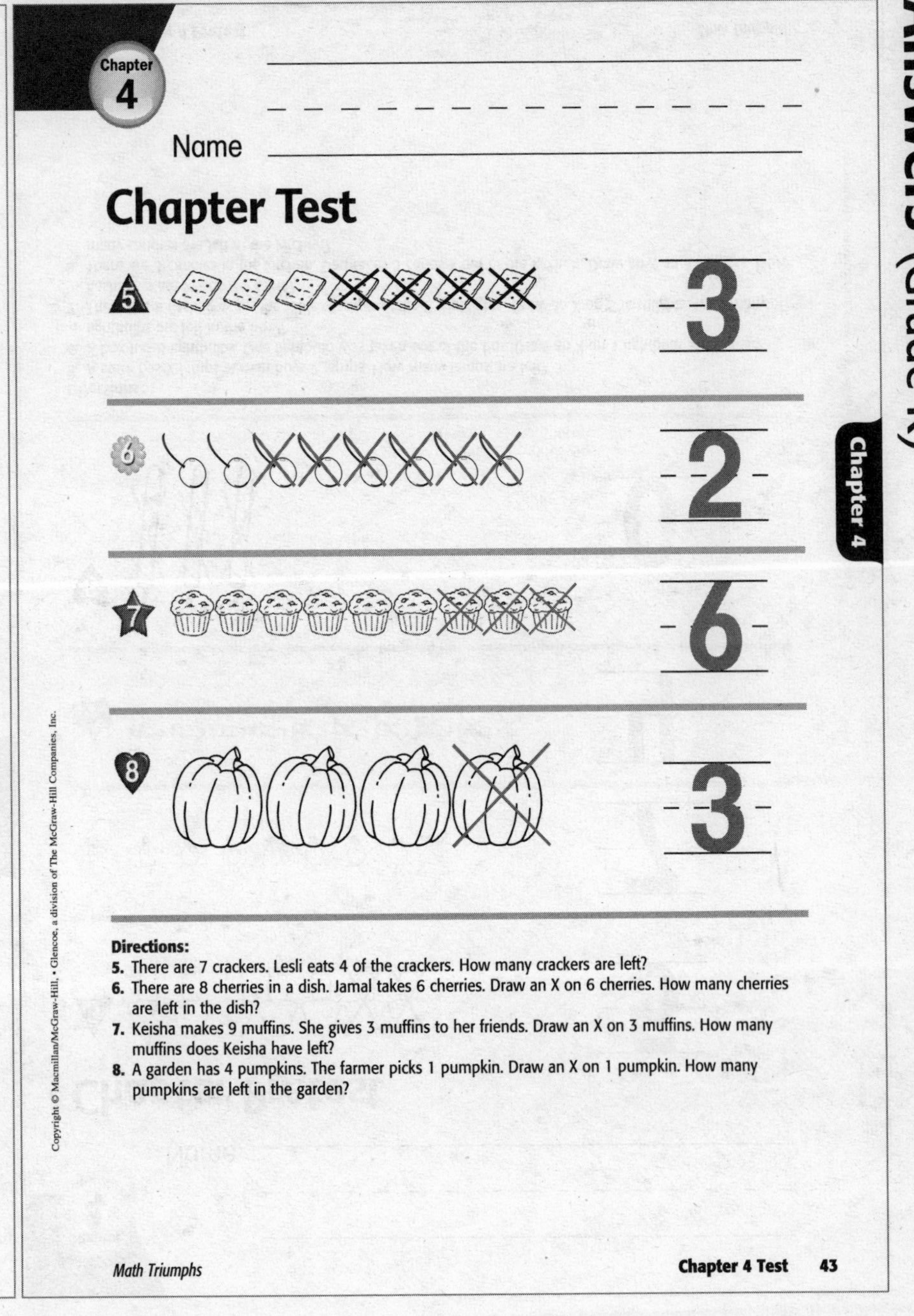

Chapter 4

Name ______________________

Chapter Test

5 — 3

6 — 2

7 — 6

8 — 3

Directions:

5. There are 7 crackers. Lesli eats 4 of the crackers. How many crackers are left?
6. There are 8 cherries in a dish. Jamal takes 6 cherries. Draw an X on 6 cherries. How many cherries are left in the dish?
7. Keisha makes 9 muffins. She gives 3 muffins to her friends. Draw an X on 3 muffins. How many muffins does Keisha have left?
8. A garden has 4 pumpkins. The farmer picks 1 pumpkin. Draw an X on 1 pumpkin. How many pumpkins are left in the garden?

Chapter 4

Name

Test Practice

1

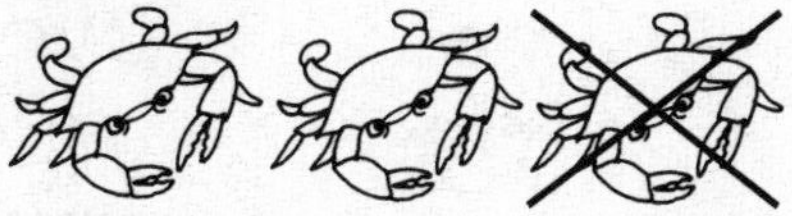

0 ○ 1 ○ 2 ●

2

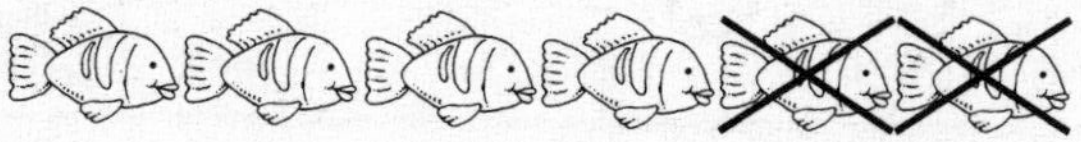

3 ○ 4 ● 5 ○

3

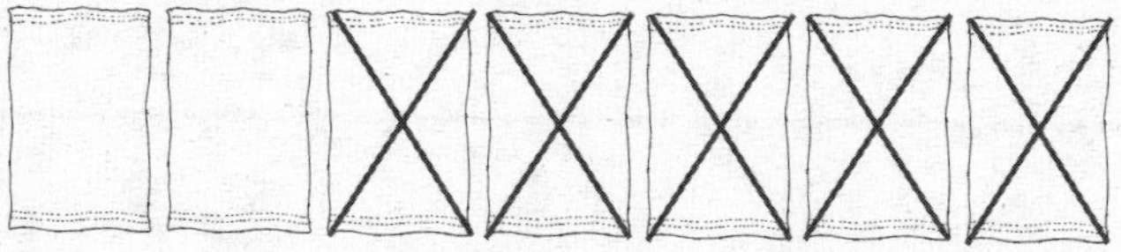

0 ○ 2 ● 6 ○

Directions:

1. There are 3 crabs on the beach. Then, 1 crab walks away. How many crabs are left on the beach?
2. There are 6 fish swimming near the beach. Then, 2 fish swim away. How many fish are left near the beach?
3. There are 7 towels in the sand. The wind blows 5 towels away. Draw an X an 5 towels. How many towels are left in the sand?

Chapter 4

Name

Test Practice

4

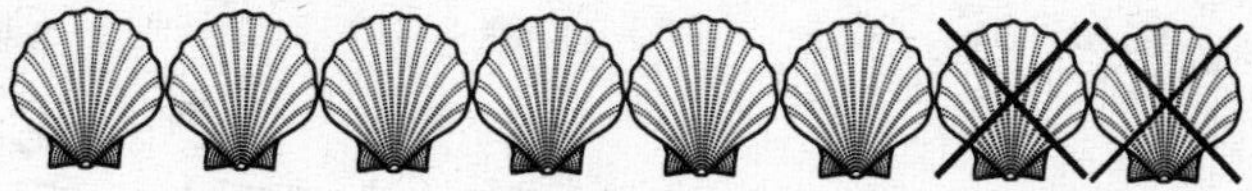

4 ○ 6 ● 7 ○

5

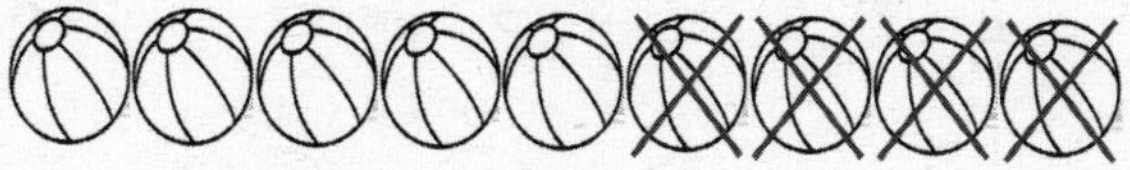

3 ○ 5 ● 7 ○

6

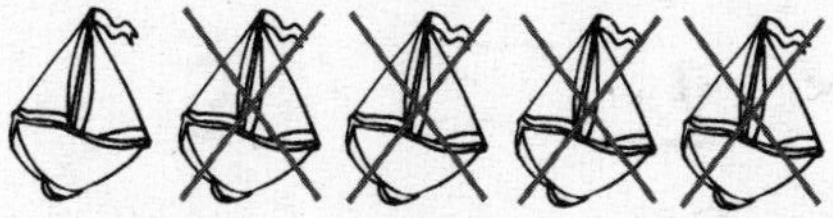

1 ● 4 ○ 9 ○

Directions:

4. Ahmed has 8 shells in his pail. He gives 2 shells to his sister. How many shells does Ahmed have left in his pail?
5. There are 9 balls on the beach. Then, 4 balls roll into the water. Draw an X on 4 balls. How many balls are left on the beach?
6. Lori has 5 boats in her pail. She puts 4 boats in the water. Draw an X on 4 boats. How many boats does Lori have left in her pail?

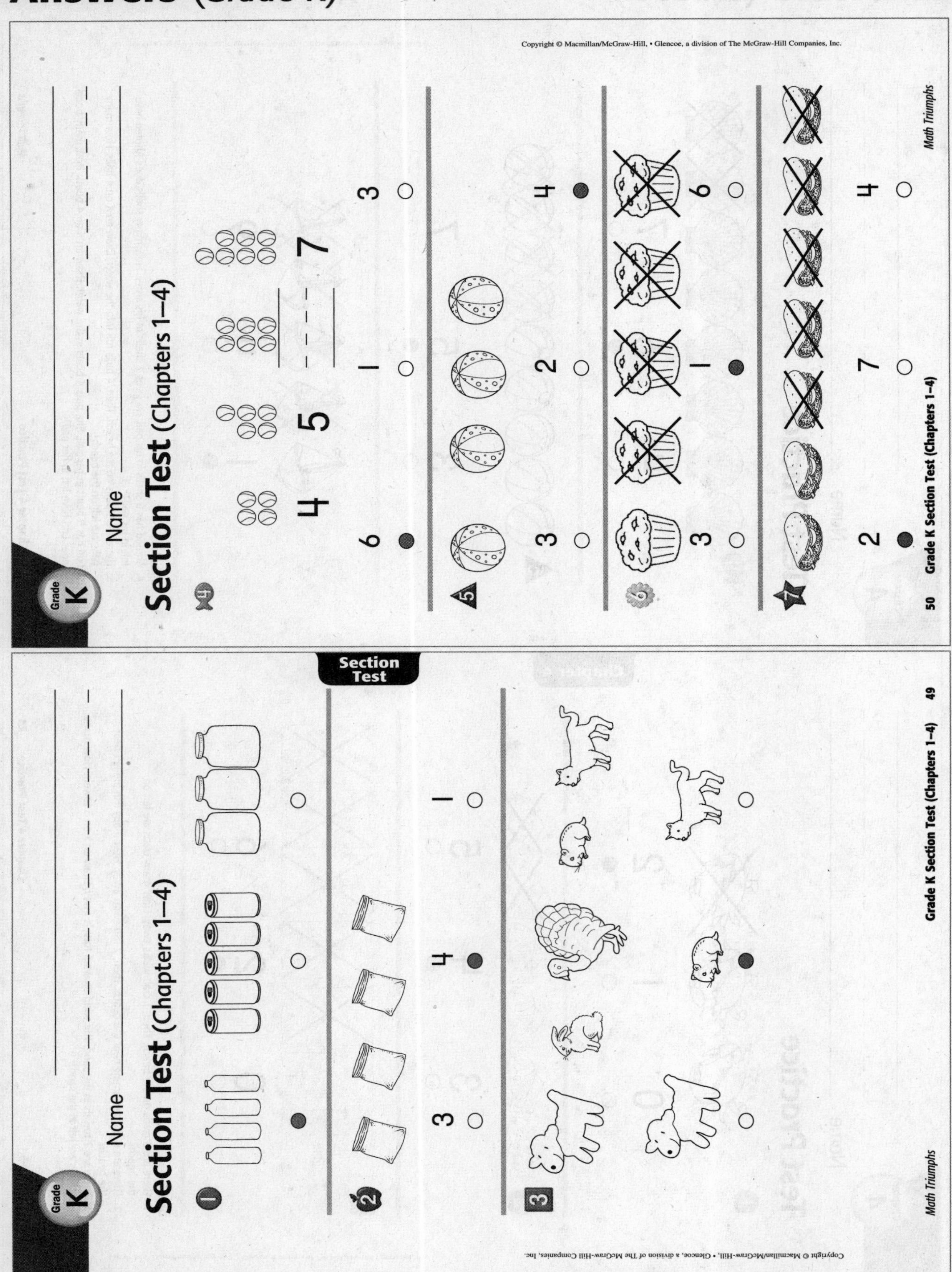
Grade K
Name
Section Test (Chapters 1–4)
4 5 7
6 1 3
3 2 4
3 1 6
2 7 4
50 Grade K Section Test (Chapters 1–4)
Math Triumphs
Copyright © Macmillan/McGraw-Hill, • Glencoe, a division of The McGraw-Hill Companies, Inc.
Grade K
Name
Section Test (Chapters 1–4)
Section Test
3 4 1
Grade K Section Test (Chapters 1–4) 49
Math Triumphs
Copyright © Macmillan/McGraw-Hill, • Glencoe, a division of The McGraw-Hill Companies, Inc.

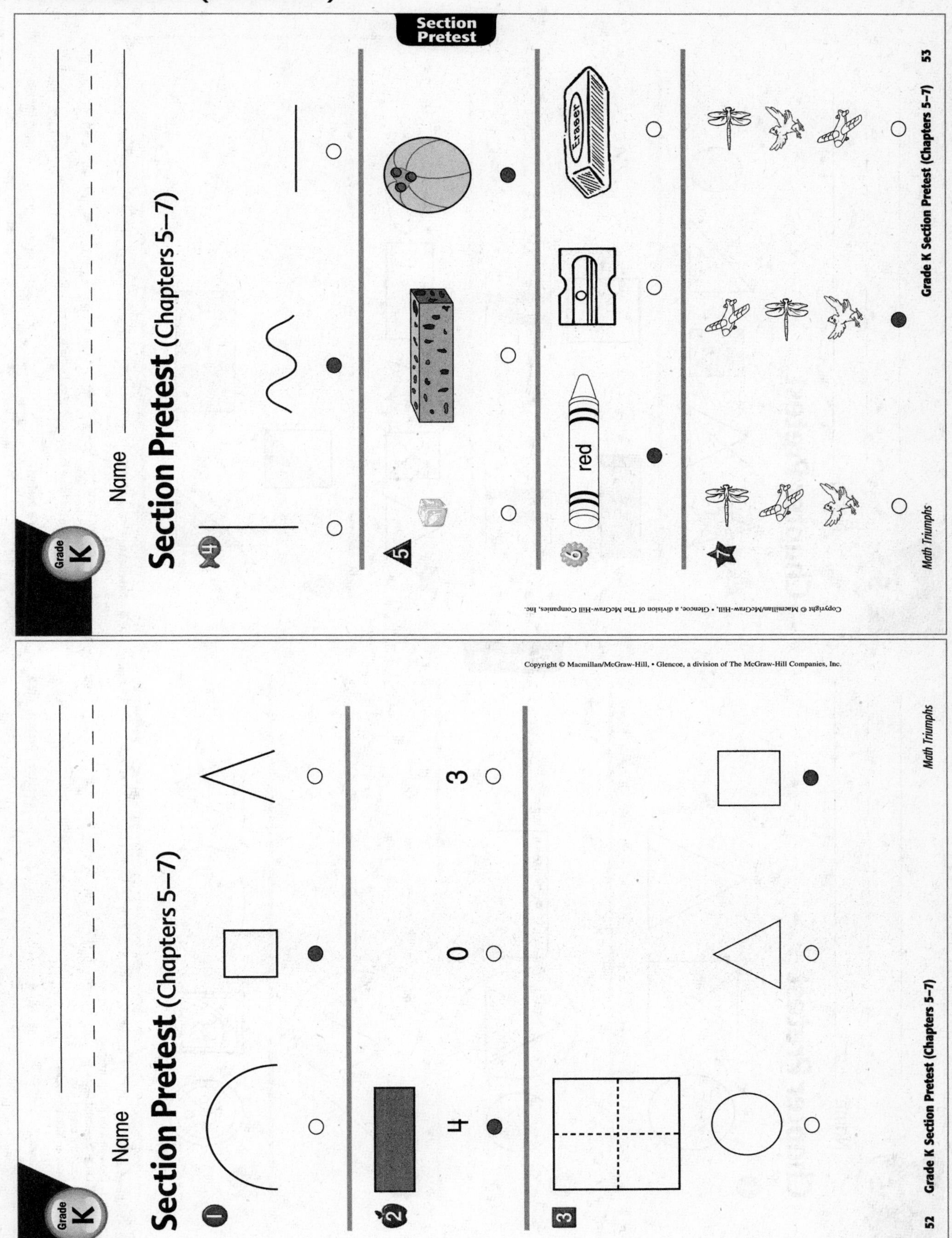

Copyright © Macmillan/McGraw-Hill, • Glencoe, a division of The McGraw-Hill Companies, Inc.
Grade K
Section Pretest (Chapters 5–7)
Name
0
4
3
52 Grade K Section Pretest (Chapters 5–7)
Math Triumphs
Section Pretest
red
Eraser
Grade K Section Pretest (Chapters 5–7) 53

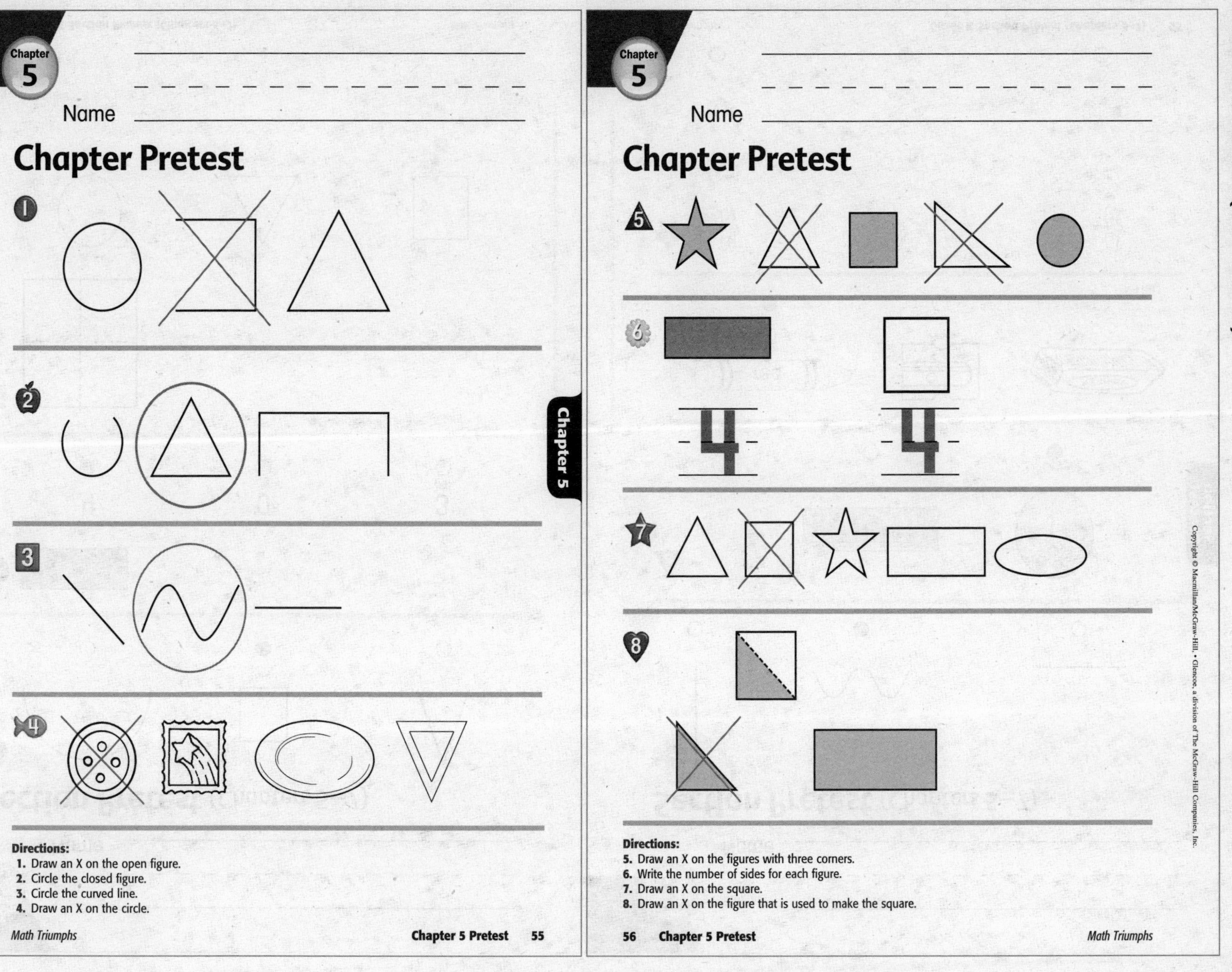

Chapter 5

Name

Chapter Pretest

Directions:
1. Draw an X on the open figure.
2. Circle the closed figure.
3. Circle the curved line.
4. Draw an X on the circle.

Math Triumphs **Chapter 5 Pretest** 55

Chapter 5

Chapter 5

Name

Chapter Pretest

Directions:
5. Draw an X on the figures with three corners.
6. Write the number of sides for each figure.
7. Draw an X on the square.
8. Draw an X on the figure that is used to make the square.

56 **Chapter 5 Pretest** *Math Triumphs*

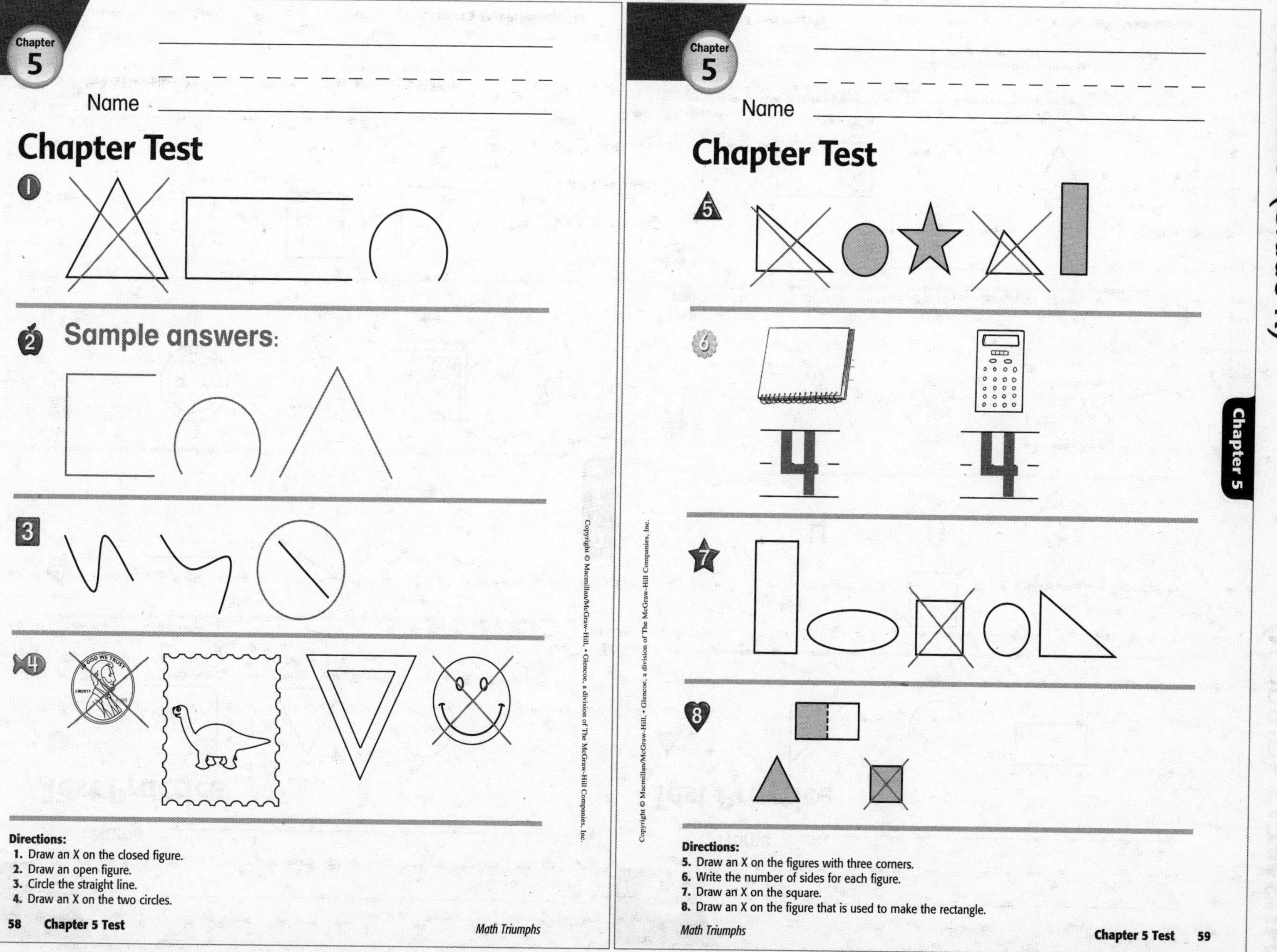

Chapter 5

Name ______

Chapter Test

1

2 Sample answers:

3

4

Directions:
1. Draw an X on the closed figure.
2. Draw an open figure.
3. Circle the straight line.
4. Draw an X on the two circles.

58 Chapter 5 Test

Math Triumphs

Chapter 5

Name ______

Chapter Test

5

6 4 4

7

8

Directions:
5. Draw an X on the figures with three corners.
6. Write the number of sides for each figure.
7. Draw an X on the square.
8. Draw an X on the figure that is used to make the rectangle.

Math Triumphs

Chapter 5 Test 59

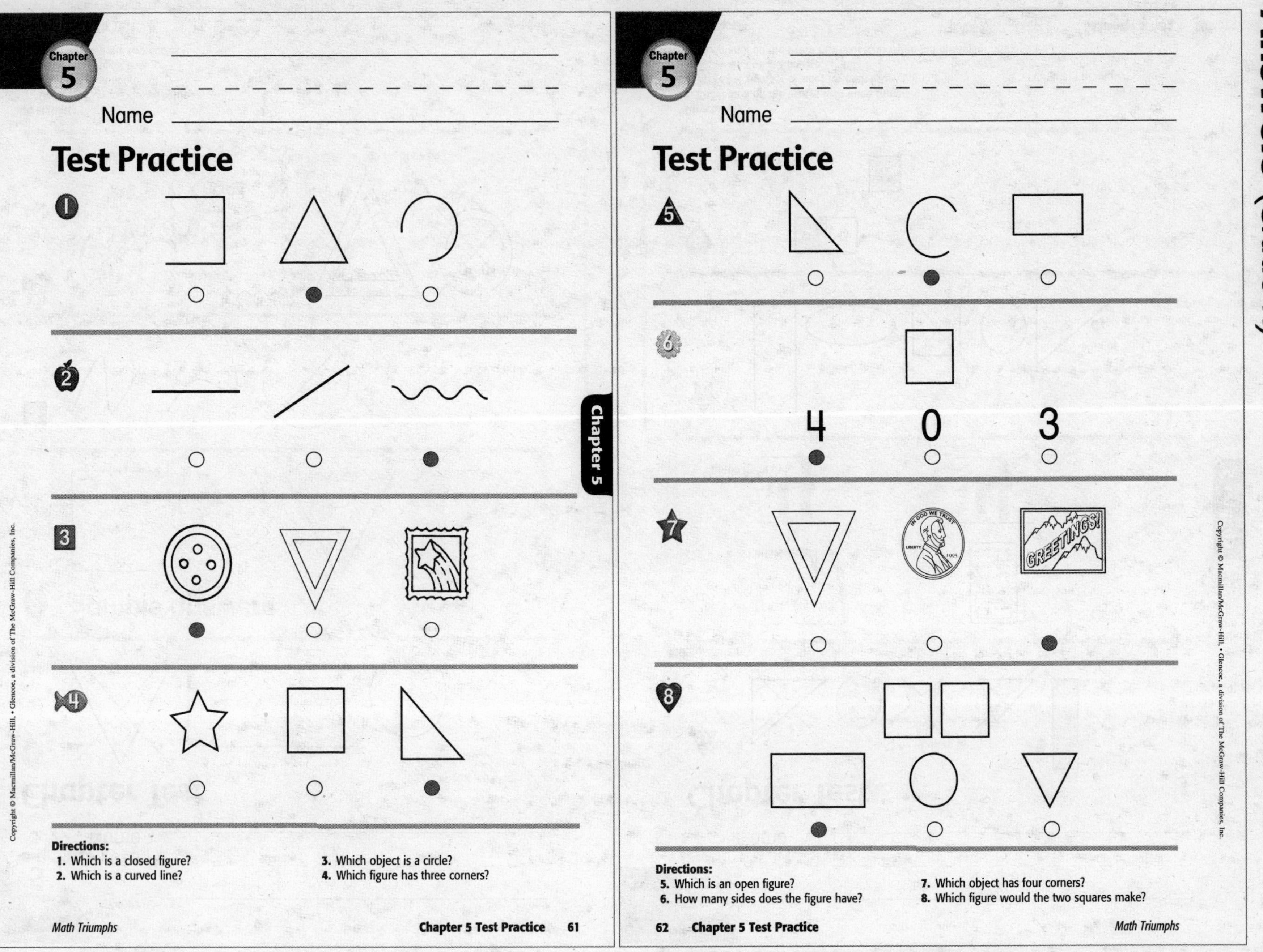

Chapter 5

Test Practice

Name ____________

1

2

3

4

Directions:
1. Which is a closed figure?
2. Which is a curved line?
3. Which object is a circle?
4. Which figure has three corners?

Math Triumphs Chapter 5 Test Practice 61

Chapter 5

Chapter 5

Test Practice

Name ____________

5

6

4 0 3

7

8

Directions:
5. Which is an open figure?
6. How many sides does the figure have?
7. Which object has four corners?
8. Which figure would the two squares make?

62 Chapter 5 Test Practice *Math Triumphs*

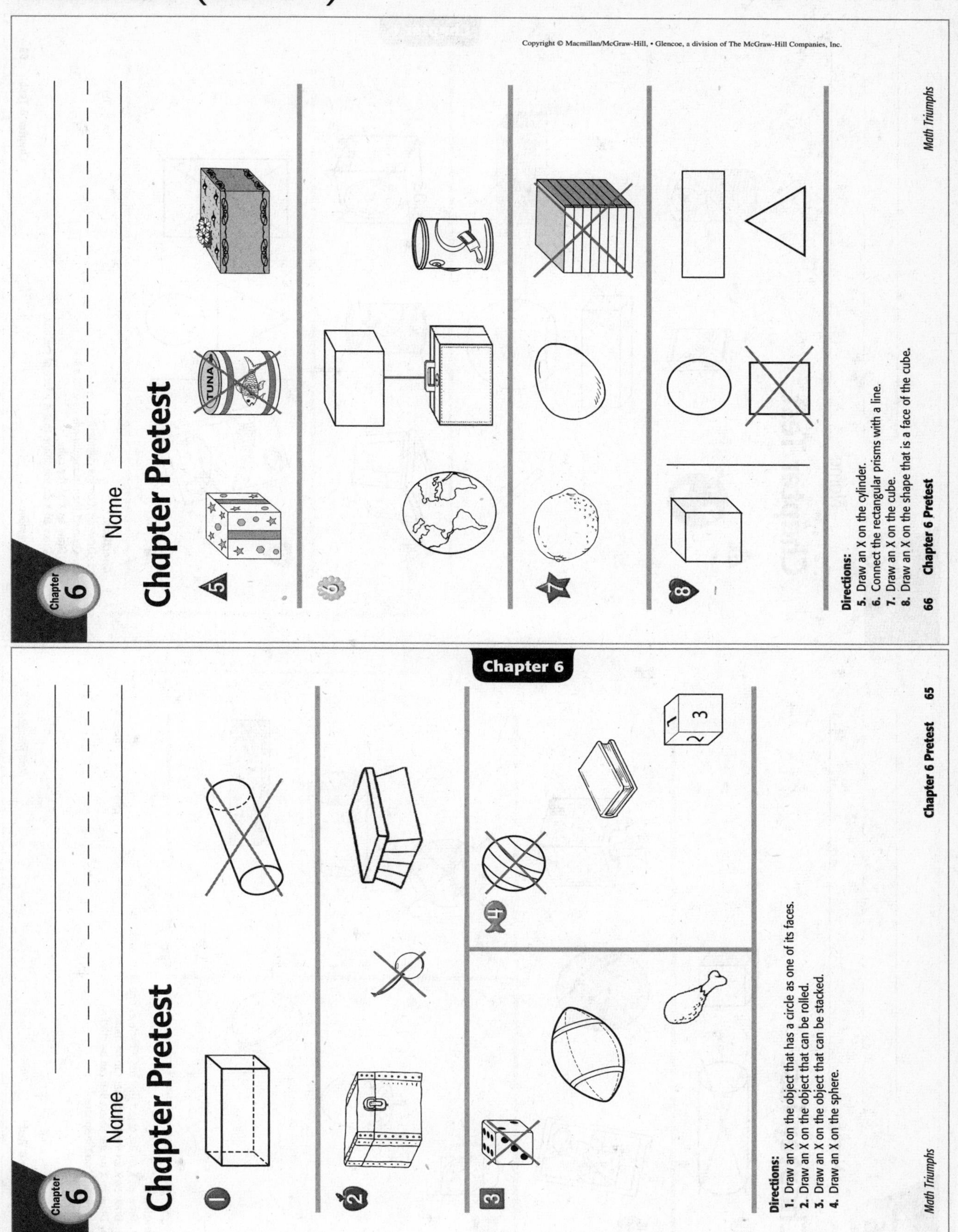

Chapter 6

Chapter 6

Name

Chapter Pretest

1 2 3 4

Directions:
1. Draw an X on the object that has a circle as one of its faces.
2. Draw an X on the object that can be rolled.
3. Draw an X on the object that can be stacked.
4. Draw an X on the sphere.

Math Triumphs Chapter 6 Pretest 65

Chapter 6

Name

Chapter Pretest

5 6 7 8

Directions:
5. Draw an X on the cylinder.
6. Connect the rectangular prisms with a line.
7. Draw an X on the cube.
8. Draw an X on the shape that is a face of the cube.

66 Chapter 6 Pretest Math Triumphs

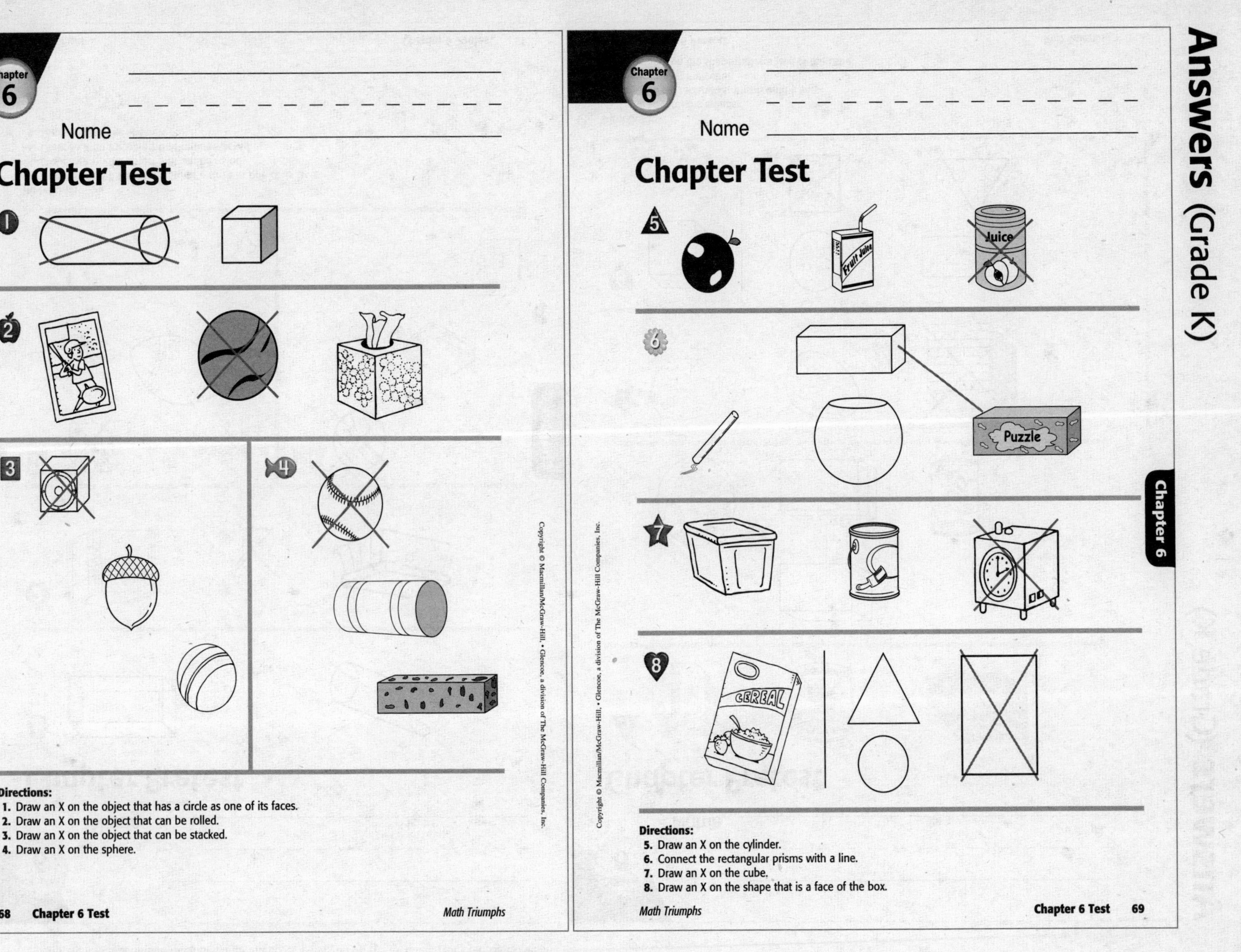

Chapter 6

Name

Chapter Test

1

2

3

4

Directions:
1. Draw an X on the object that has a circle as one of its faces.
2. Draw an X on the object that can be rolled.
3. Draw an X on the object that can be stacked.
4. Draw an X on the sphere.

68 Chapter 6 Test *Math Triumphs*

Chapter 6

Name

Chapter Test

5

6

7

8

Directions:
5. Draw an X on the cylinder.
6. Connect the rectangular prisms with a line.
7. Draw an X on the cube.
8. Draw an X on the shape that is a face of the box.

Math Triumphs Chapter 6 Test 69

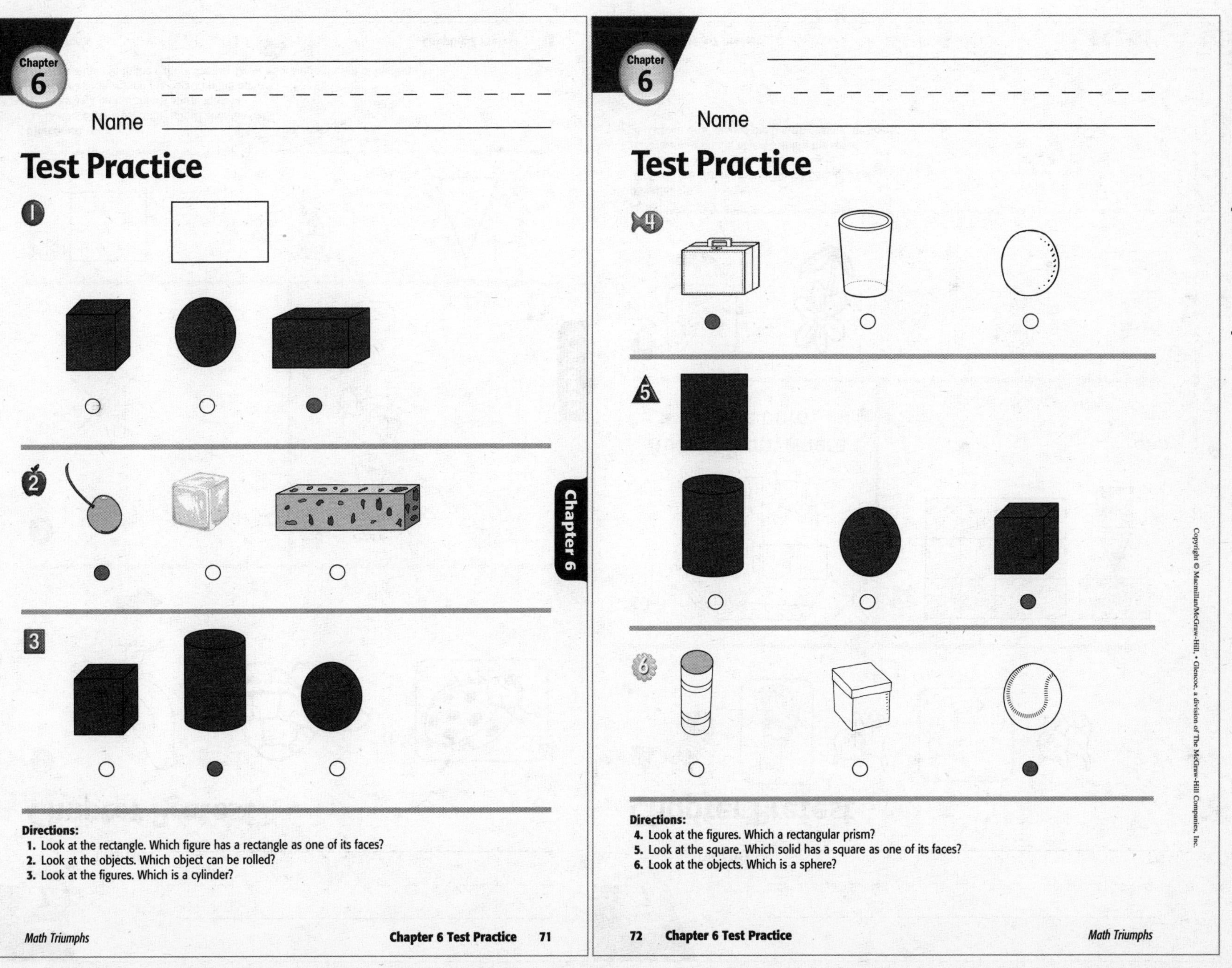

Chapter 6

Name

Test Practice

1

2

3

Directions:
1. Look at the rectangle. Which figure has a rectangle as one of its faces?
2. Look at the objects. Which object can be rolled?
3. Look at the figures. Which is a cylinder?

Math Triumphs **Chapter 6 Test Practice 71**

Chapter 6

Name

Test Practice

4

5

6

Directions:
4. Look at the figures. Which a rectangular prism?
5. Look at the square. Which solid has a square as one of its faces?
6. Look at the objects. Which is a sphere?

72 Chapter 6 Test Practice *Math Triumphs*

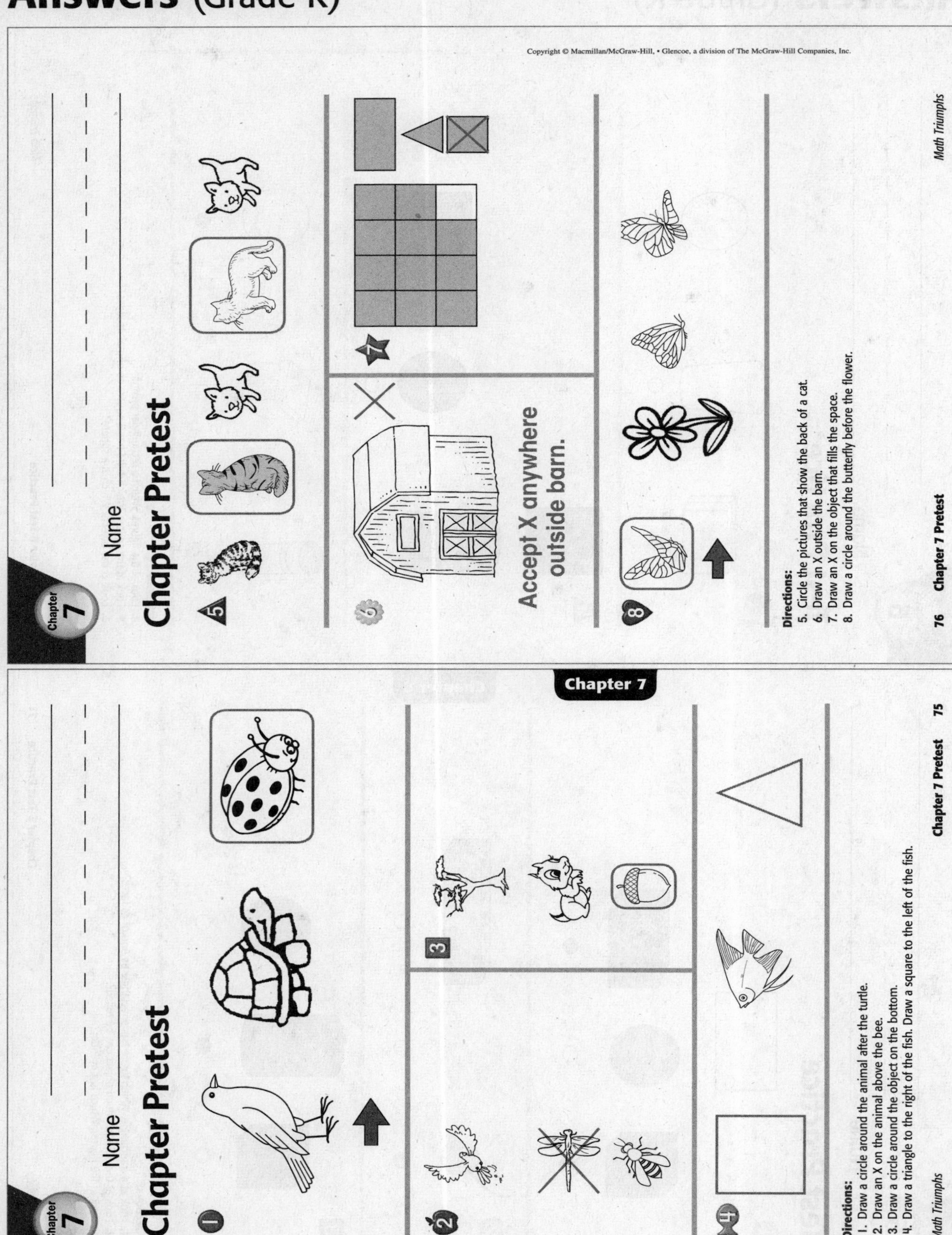

Chapter 7

Name ____________________

Chapter Pretest

1

2

3

4

Directions:
1. Draw a circle around the animal after the turtle.
2. Draw an X on the animal above the bee.
3. Draw a circle around the object on the bottom.
4. Draw a triangle to the right of the fish. Draw a square to the left of the fish.

Math Triumphs Chapter 7 Pretest 75

Chapter 7

Name ____________________

Chapter Pretest

5

6

Accept X anywhere outside barn.

7

8

Directions:
5. Circle the pictures that show the back of a cat.
6. Draw an X outside the barn.
7. Draw an X on the object that fills the space.
8. Draw a circle around the butterfly before the flower.

76 Chapter 7 Pretest *Math Triumphs*

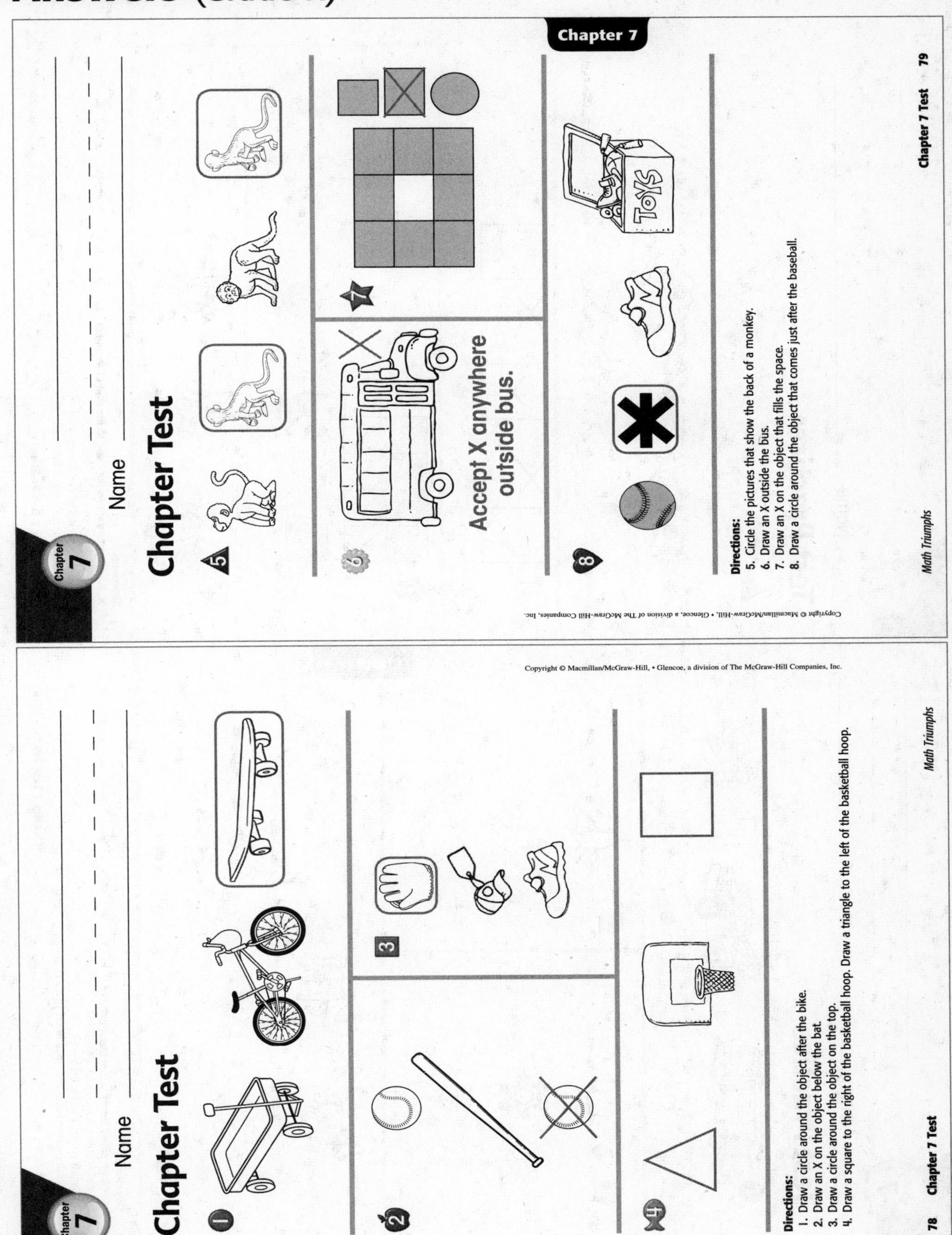

Chapter 7

Name

Chapter Test

1

2

3

4

Directions:
1. Draw a circle around the object after the bike.
2. Draw an X on the object below the bat.
3. Draw a circle around the object on the top.
4. Draw a square to the right of the basketball hoop. Draw a triangle to the left of the basketball hoop.

78 **Chapter 7 Test** *Math Triumphs*

Copyright © Macmillan/McGraw-Hill, • Glencoe, a division of The McGraw-Hill Companies, Inc.

Chapter 7

Name

Chapter Test

5

6

Accept X anywhere outside bus.

7

8

Directions:
5. Circle the pictures that show the back of a monkey.
6. Draw an X outside the bus.
7. Draw an X on the object that fills the space.
8. Draw a circle around the object that comes just after the baseball.

Math Triumphs **Chapter 7 Test** 79

Copyright © Macmillan/McGraw-Hill, • Glencoe, a division of The McGraw-Hill Companies, Inc.

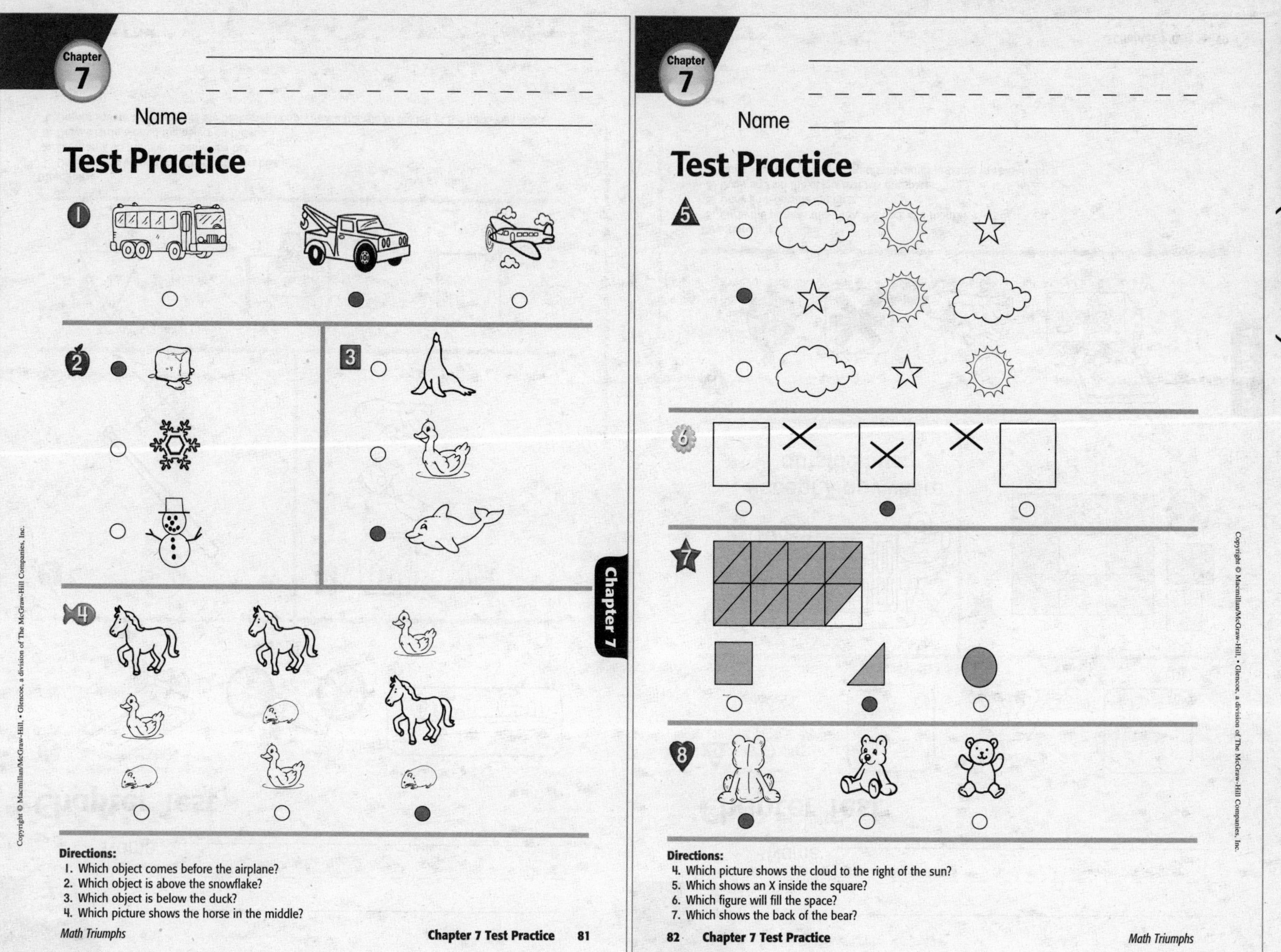

Chapter 7

Name

Test Practice

Directions:
1. Which object comes before the airplane?
2. Which object is above the snowflake?
3. Which object is below the duck?
4. Which picture shows the horse in the middle?

Math Triumphs

Chapter 7 Test Practice 81

Chapter 7

Name

Test Practice

Directions:
4. Which picture shows the cloud to the right of the sun?
5. Which shows an X inside the square?
6. Which figure will fill the space?
7. Which shows the back of the bear?

82 Chapter 7 Test Practice

Math Triumphs

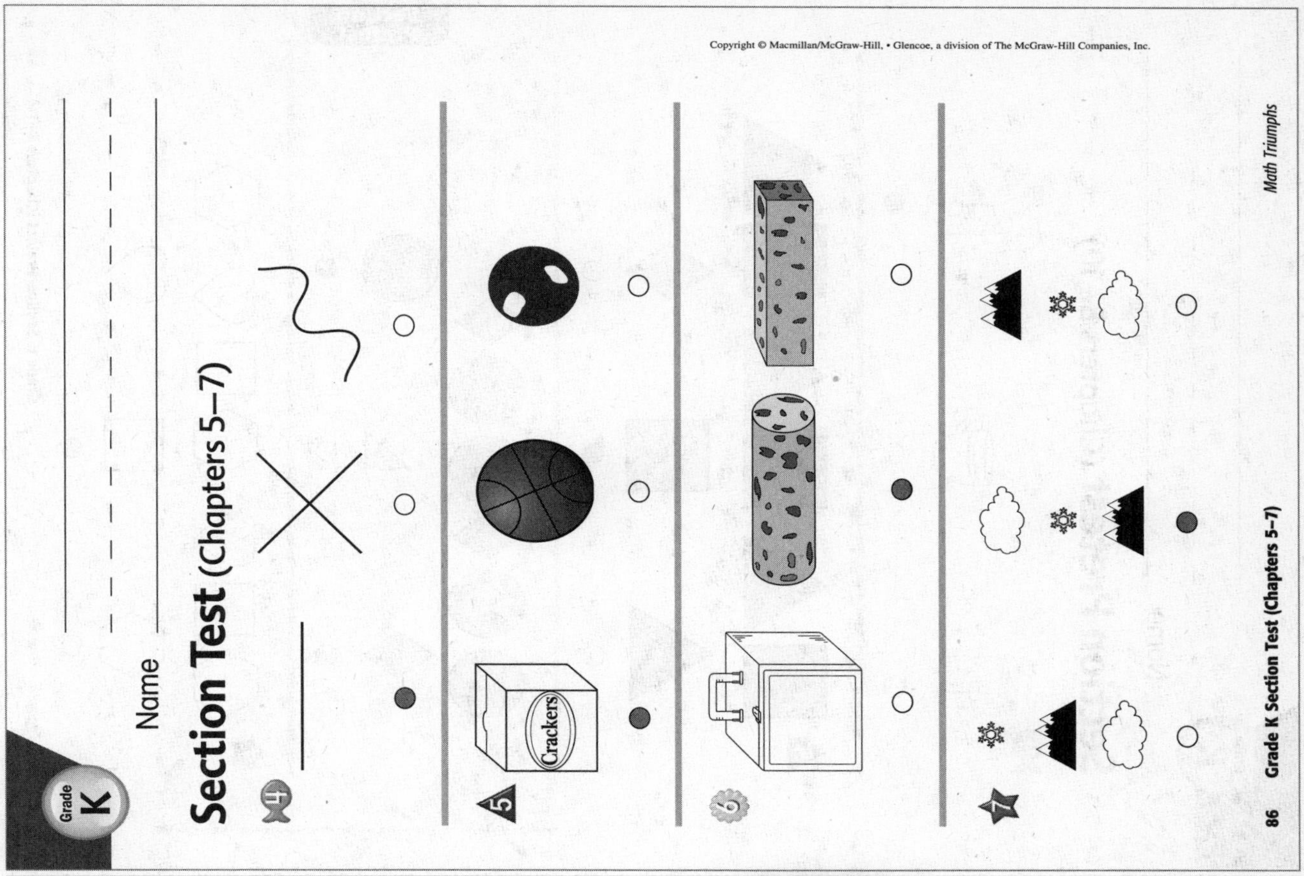

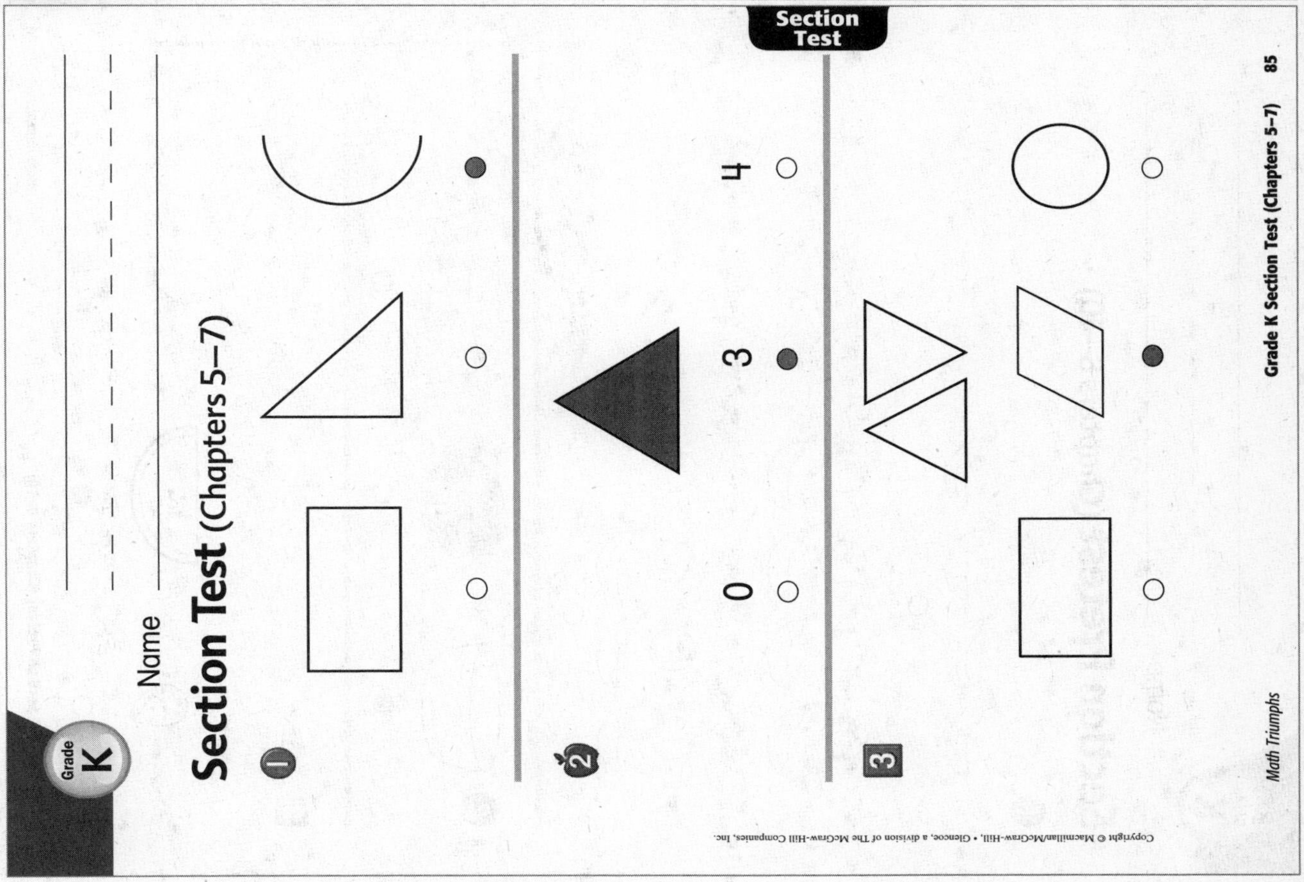

Grade K

Name ______________________

Section Test (Chapters 5–7)

1

○ ○ ●

2

0 3 4

○ ● ○

3

○ ● ○

Section Test

Grade K

Name ______________________

Section Test (Chapters 5–7)

4

● ○ ○

5

Crackers

● ○ ○

6

○ ● ○

7

○ ● ○

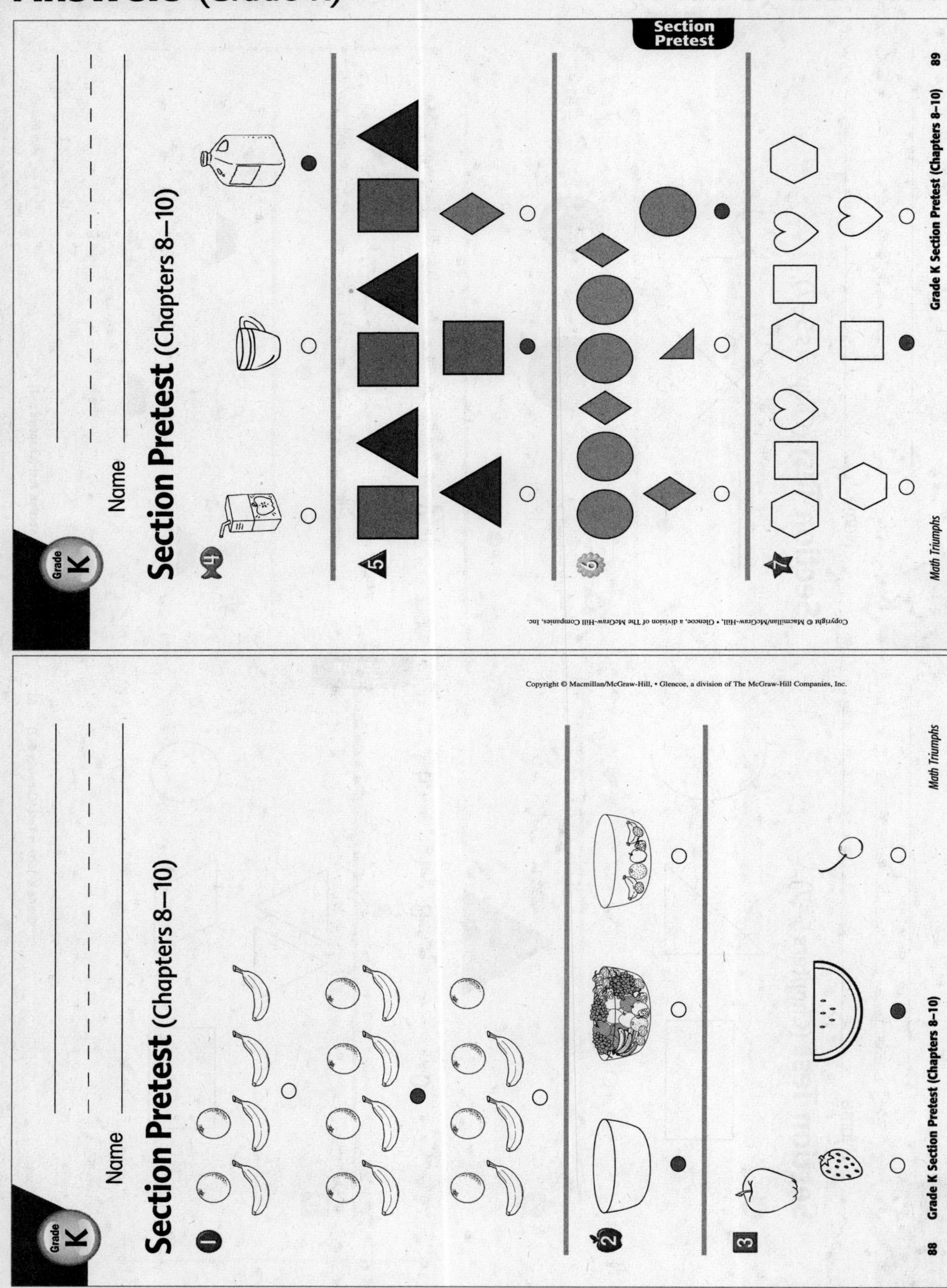
Grade K
Name
Section Pretest (Chapters 8–10)
88 Grade K Section Pretest (Chapters 8–10)
Math Triumphs
Copyright © Macmillan/McGraw-Hill, • Glencoe, a division of The McGraw-Hill Companies, Inc.
Section Pretest
Grade K Section Pretest (Chapters 8–10) 89

Chapter 8

Name

Chapter Pretest

1

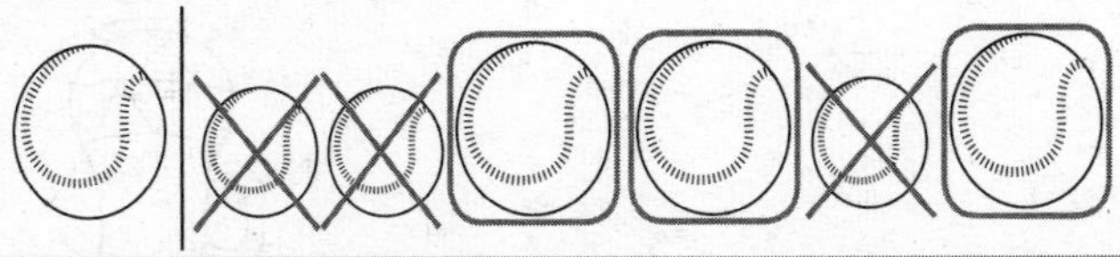

2

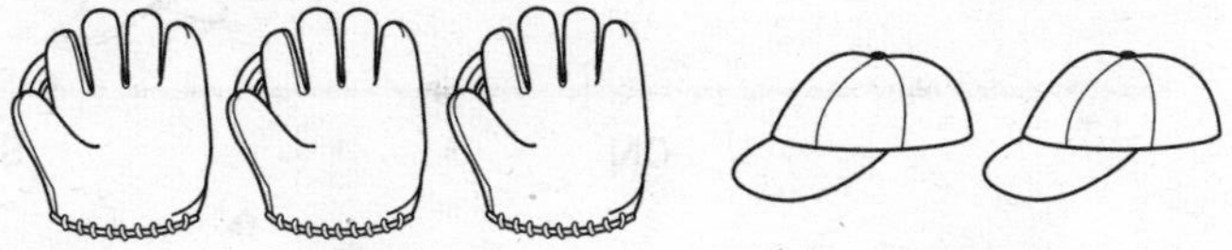

3 Yes

2 (No)

3

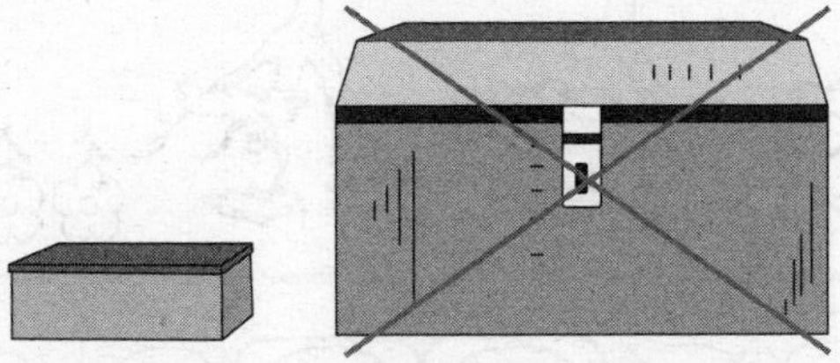

Chapter 8

Directions:

1. Look at the first ball. Circle the balls that are the same size as the first ball. Draw an X on the balls that are a different size.
2. Count the mitts. Write how many. Count the caps. Write how many. Is the number of mitts equal to the number of caps? Circle Yes or No.
3. The box holds 6 balls. The chest holds 60 balls. Put an X on the container that holds more.

Chapter 8

Name

Chapter Pretest

4

5

6

Check students' drawings.

7

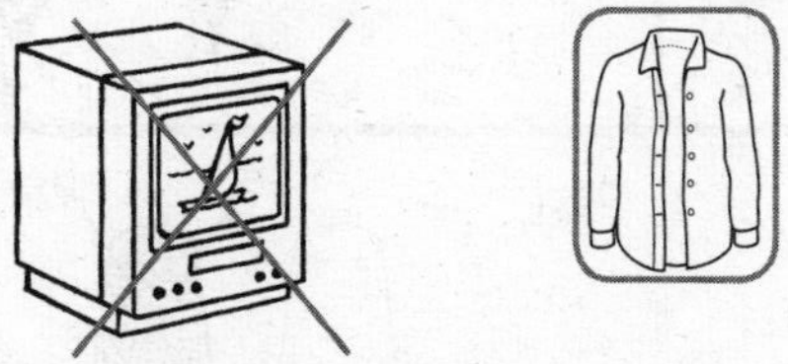

Directions:

4. Draw an X on the empty bucket.
5. Circle the tall mop.
6. Jan and Adam are helping their dad wash the clothes. They are filling the basket shown. Draw a basket that will hold less than the basket Jan and Adam are using.
7. Circle the light object. Draw an X on the heavy object.

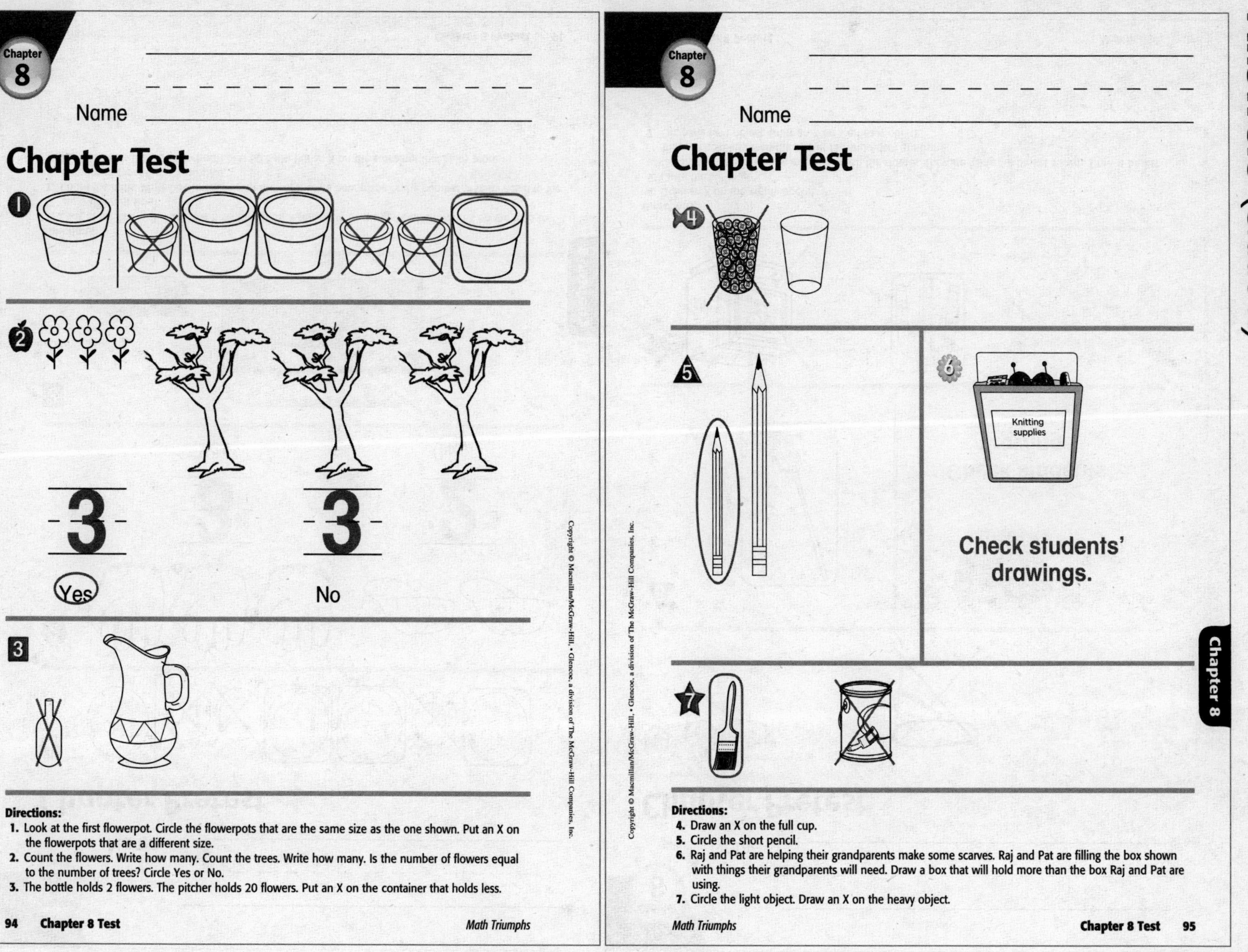

Chapter 8

Name

Chapter Test

1

2

3 3

Yes No

3

Directions:
1. Look at the first flowerpot. Circle the flowerpots that are the same size as the one shown. Put an X on the flowerpots that are a different size.
2. Count the flowers. Write how many. Count the trees. Write how many. Is the number of flowers equal to the number of trees? Circle Yes or No.
3. The bottle holds 2 flowers. The pitcher holds 20 flowers. Put an X on the container that holds less.

94 Chapter 8 Test *Math Triumphs*

Chapter 8

Name

Chapter Test

4

5

6

Check students' drawings.

7

Directions:
4. Draw an X on the full cup.
5. Circle the short pencil.
6. Raj and Pat are helping their grandparents make some scarves. Raj and Pat are filling the box shown with things their grandparents will need. Draw a box that will hold more than the box Raj and Pat are using.
7. Circle the light object. Draw an X on the heavy object.

Math Triumphs Chapter 8 Test 95

Chapter 8

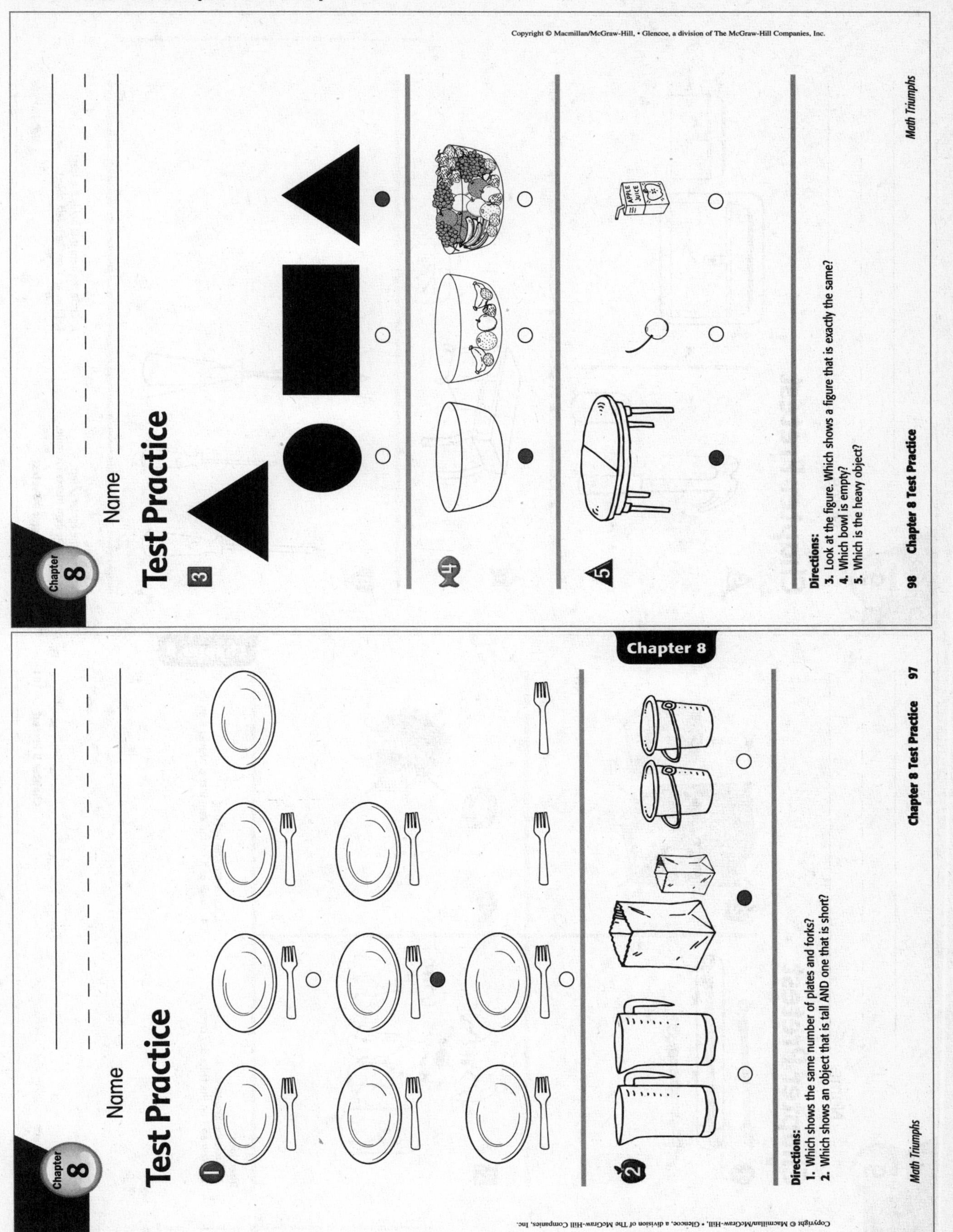
Chapter 8
Name
Test Practice
1
2
Directions:
1. Which shows the same number of plates and forks?
2. Which shows an object that is tall AND one that is short?
Math Triumphs
Chapter 8 Test Practice 97
Chapter 8
Copyright © Macmillan/McGraw-Hill, • Glencoe, a division of The McGraw-Hill Companies, Inc.
Chapter 8
Name
Test Practice
3
4
5
APPLE JUICE
Directions:
3. Look at the figure. Which shows a figure that is exactly the same?
4. Which bowl is empty?
5. Which is the heavy object?
98 Chapter 8 Test Practice
Math Triumphs
Copyright © Macmillan/McGraw-Hill, • Glencoe, a division of The McGraw-Hill Companies, Inc.

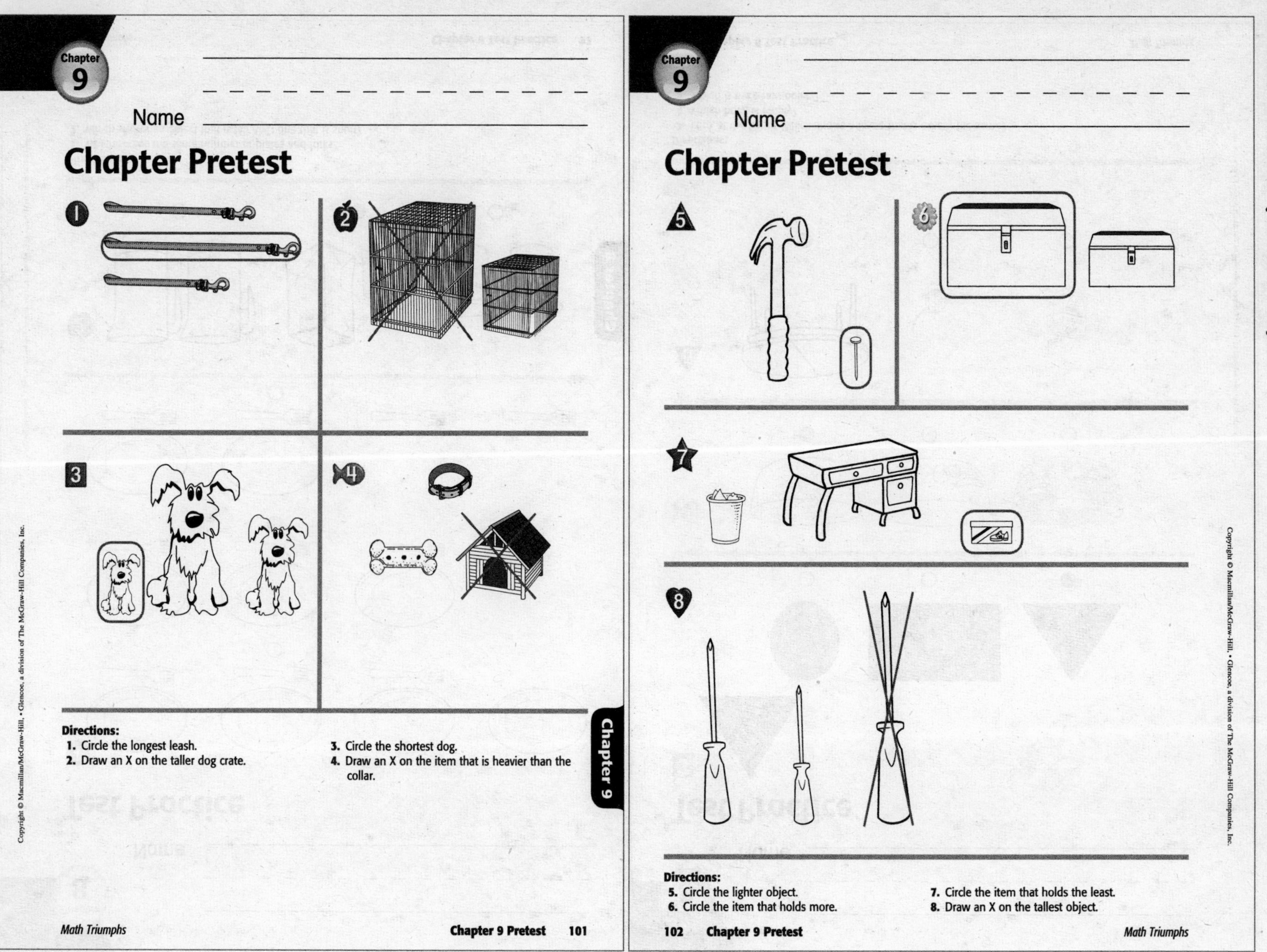

Chapter 9

Name

Chapter Pretest

Directions:
1. Circle the longest leash.
2. Draw an X on the taller dog crate.
3. Circle the shortest dog.
4. Draw an X on the item that is heavier than the collar.

Chapter 9

Name

Chapter Pretest

Directions:
5. Circle the lighter object.
6. Circle the item that holds more.
7. Circle the item that holds the least.
8. Draw an X on the tallest object.

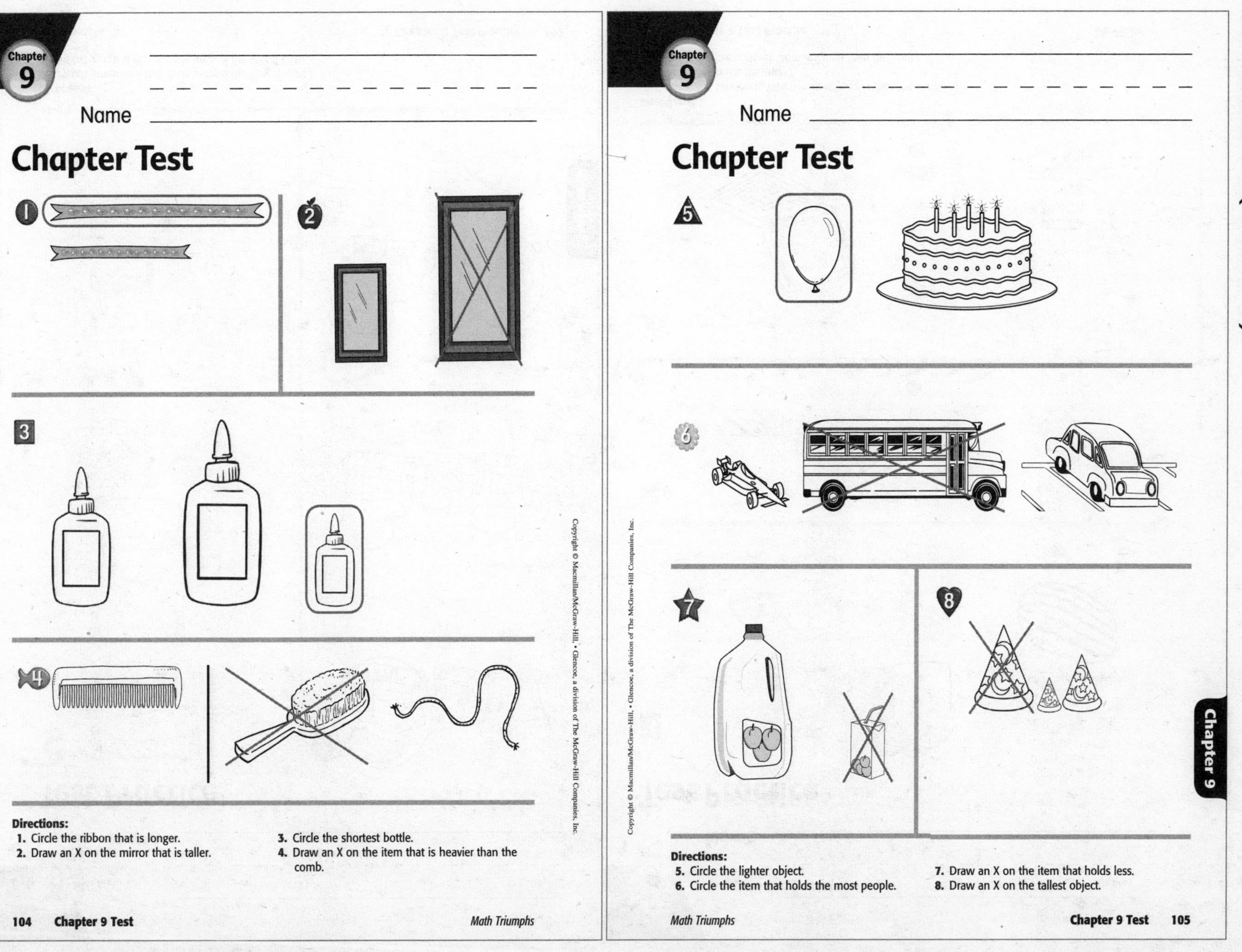

Chapter 9

Name

Chapter Test

1

2

3

4

Directions:
1. Circle the ribbon that is longer.
2. Draw an X on the mirror that is taller.
3. Circle the shortest bottle.
4. Draw an X on the item that is heavier than the comb.

Chapter 9

Name

Chapter Test

5

6

7

8

Directions:
5. Circle the lighter object.
6. Circle the item that holds the most people.
7. Draw an X on the item that holds less.
8. Draw an X on the tallest object.

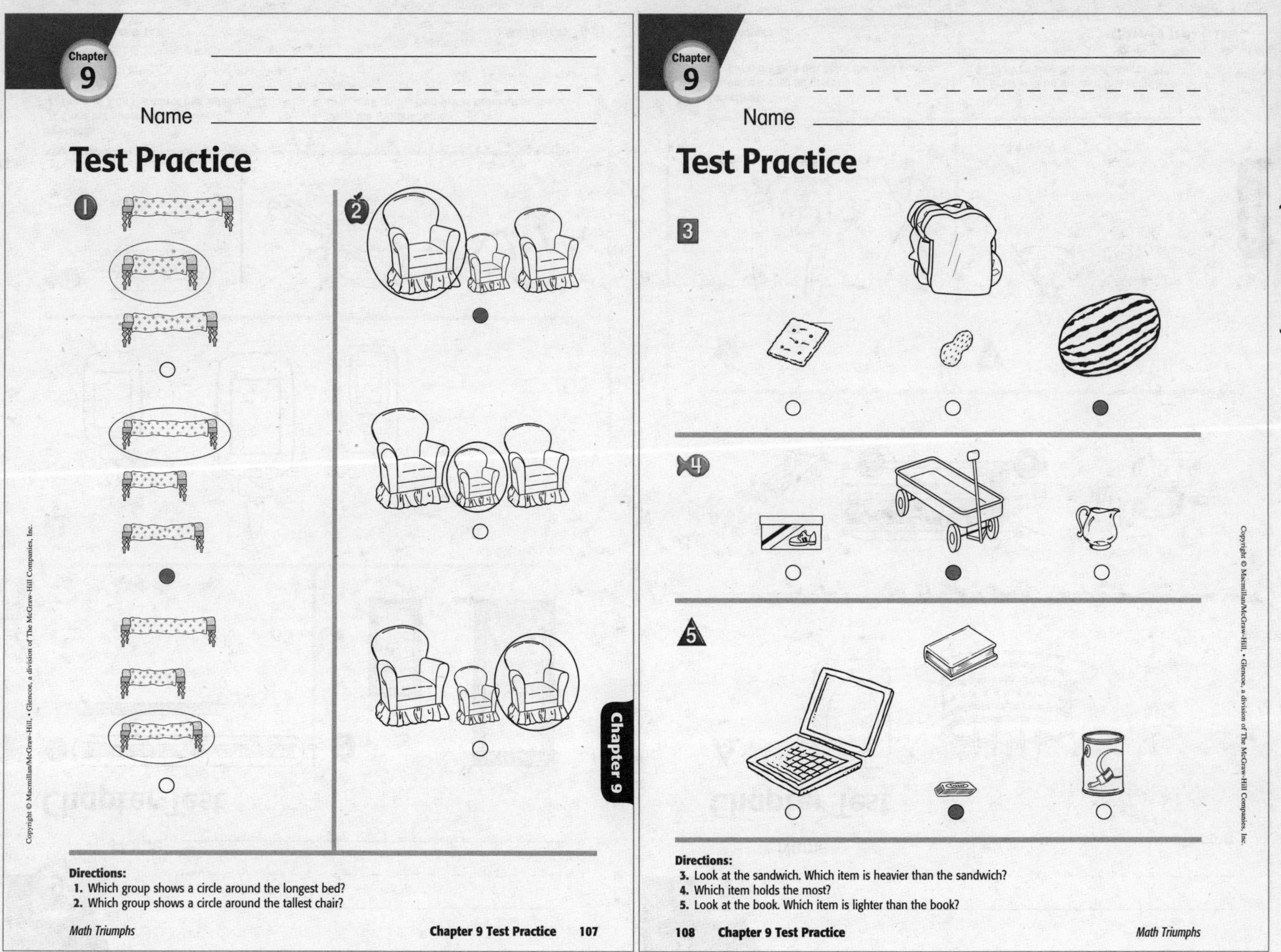
Chapter 9
Name
Test Practice
Directions:
1. Which group shows a circle around the longest bed?
2. Which group shows a circle around the tallest chair?
Math Triumphs
Chapter 9 Test Practice 107
Chapter 9
Copyright © Macmillan/McGraw-Hill, • Glencoe, a division of The McGraw-Hill Companies, Inc.
Chapter 9
Name
Test Practice
Directions:
3. Look at the sandwich. Which item is heavier than the sandwich?
4. Which item holds the most?
5. Look at the book. Which item is lighter than the book?
108 Chapter 9 Test Practice
Math Triumphs
Copyright © Macmillan/McGraw-Hill, • Glencoe, a division of The McGraw-Hill Companies, Inc.

Chapter 10

Name

Chapter Pretest

1

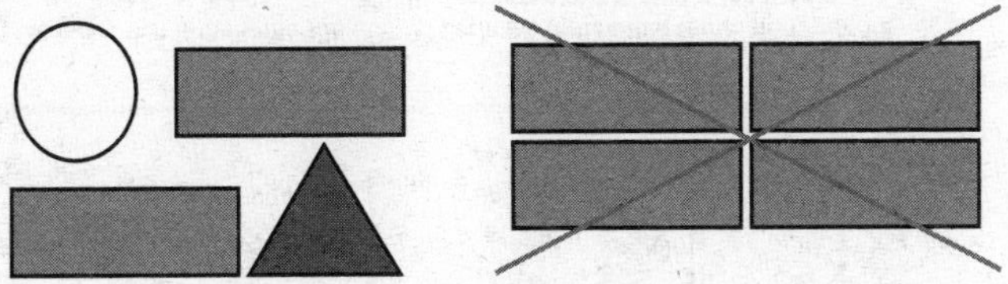

2

3

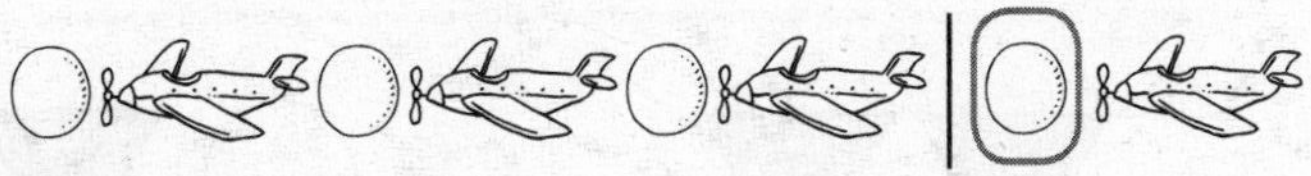

4

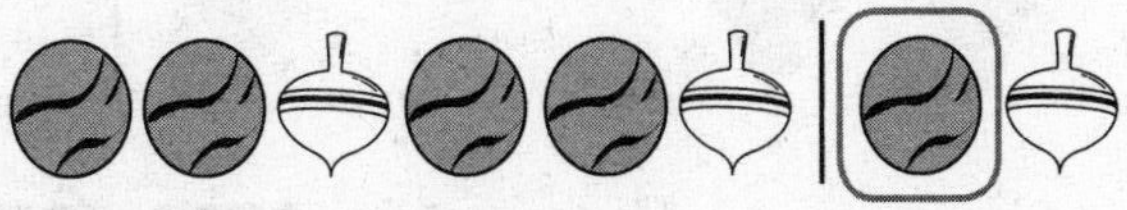

Directions:

1. Draw an X on the group that is the same size and shape.
2. Circle the toy that belongs in the group.
3. Circle what comes next in the pattern.
4. Circle what comes next in the pattern.

Chapter 10

Chapter 10

Name

Chapter Pretest

5

6

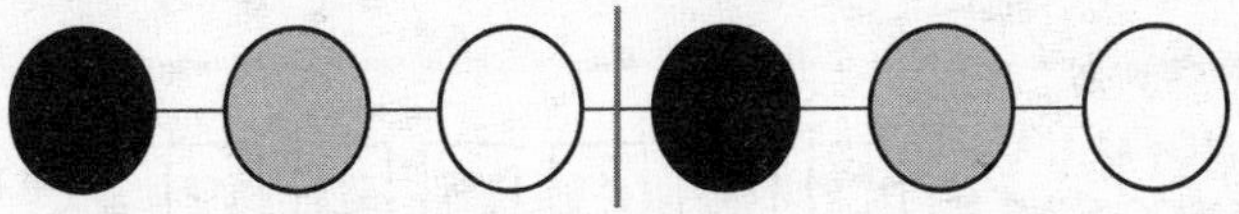

7

8 | 1 | 2 | 1 | 2 | 1 | 2 | Accept any AB pattern with numbers.

9 | S | T | T | S | T | T | Accept any ABB pattern with letters.

Directions:

5. Look at the pattern. Draw the shape that comes next.
6. Draw a line to show where the pattern starts over, or repeats.
7. Circle the picture that comes next.
8. Choose two numbers. Make an AB pattern.
9. Choose two letters. Make an ABB pattern.

Chapter 10

Name

Chapter Test

1

2

3

4

Directions:

1. Draw an X on the group that is the same size and shape.
2. Circle the item that belongs in the group.
3. Circle the picture that comes next.
4. Circle what comes next in the pattern.

Chapter 10

Name

Chapter Test

5

6

7

8 A B A B A B

Accept any AB pattern with letters.

9 2 1 1 2 1 1

Accept any ABB pattern with numbers.

Directions:

5. Look at the pattern. Draw the next shape.
6. Draw a line to show where the pattern starts over, or repeats.
7. Circle what comes next in the pattern.
8. Choose two letters. Make an AB pattern.
9. Choose two numbers. Make an ABB pattern.

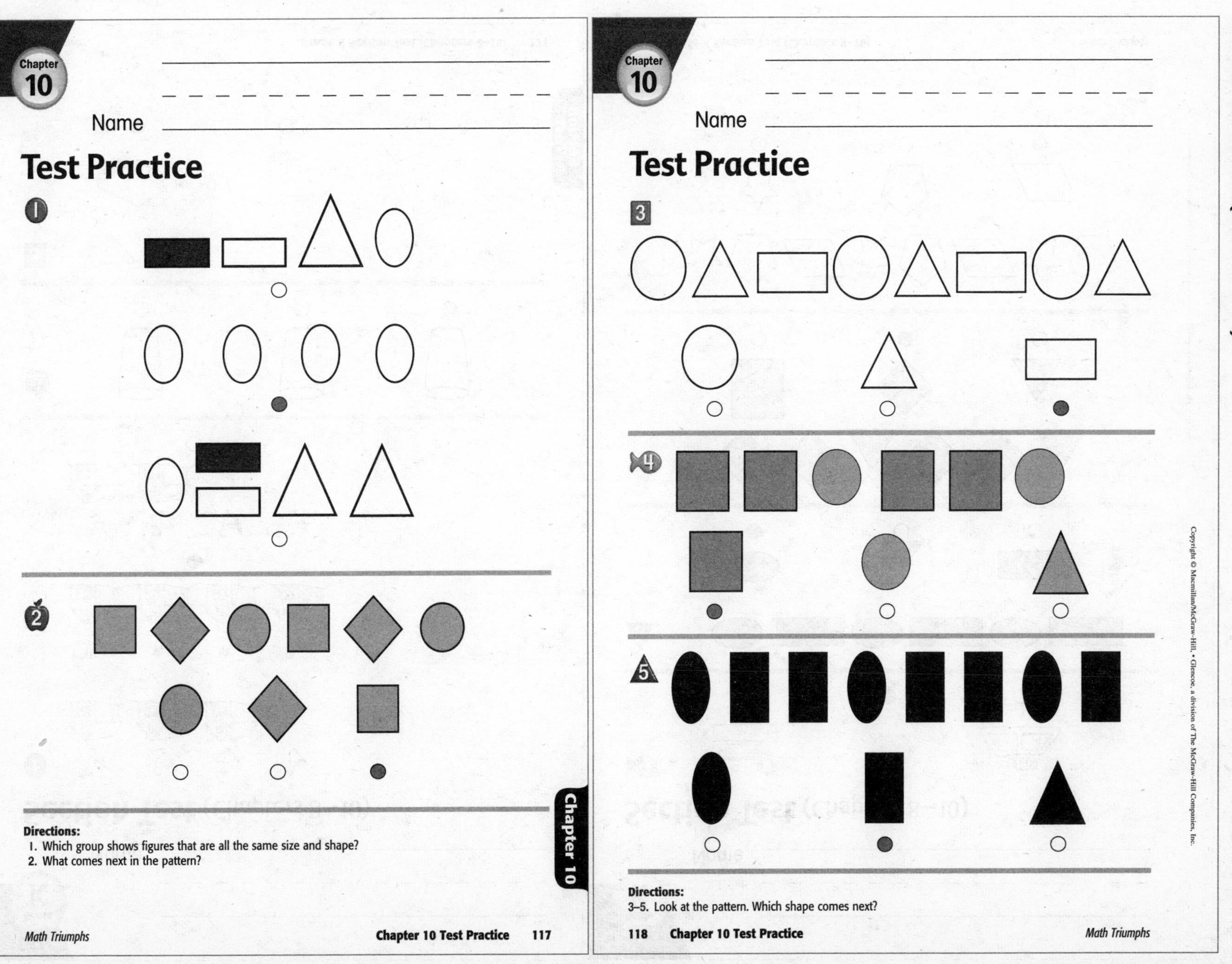

Chapter 10

Name

Test Practice

1

2

Directions:
1. Which group shows figures that are all the same size and shape?
2. What comes next in the pattern?

Math Triumphs Chapter 10 Test Practice 117

Chapter 10

Chapter 10

Name

Test Practice

3

4

5

Directions:
3–5. Look at the pattern. Which shape comes next?

118 Chapter 10 Test Practice *Math Triumphs*

Answers (Grade K)

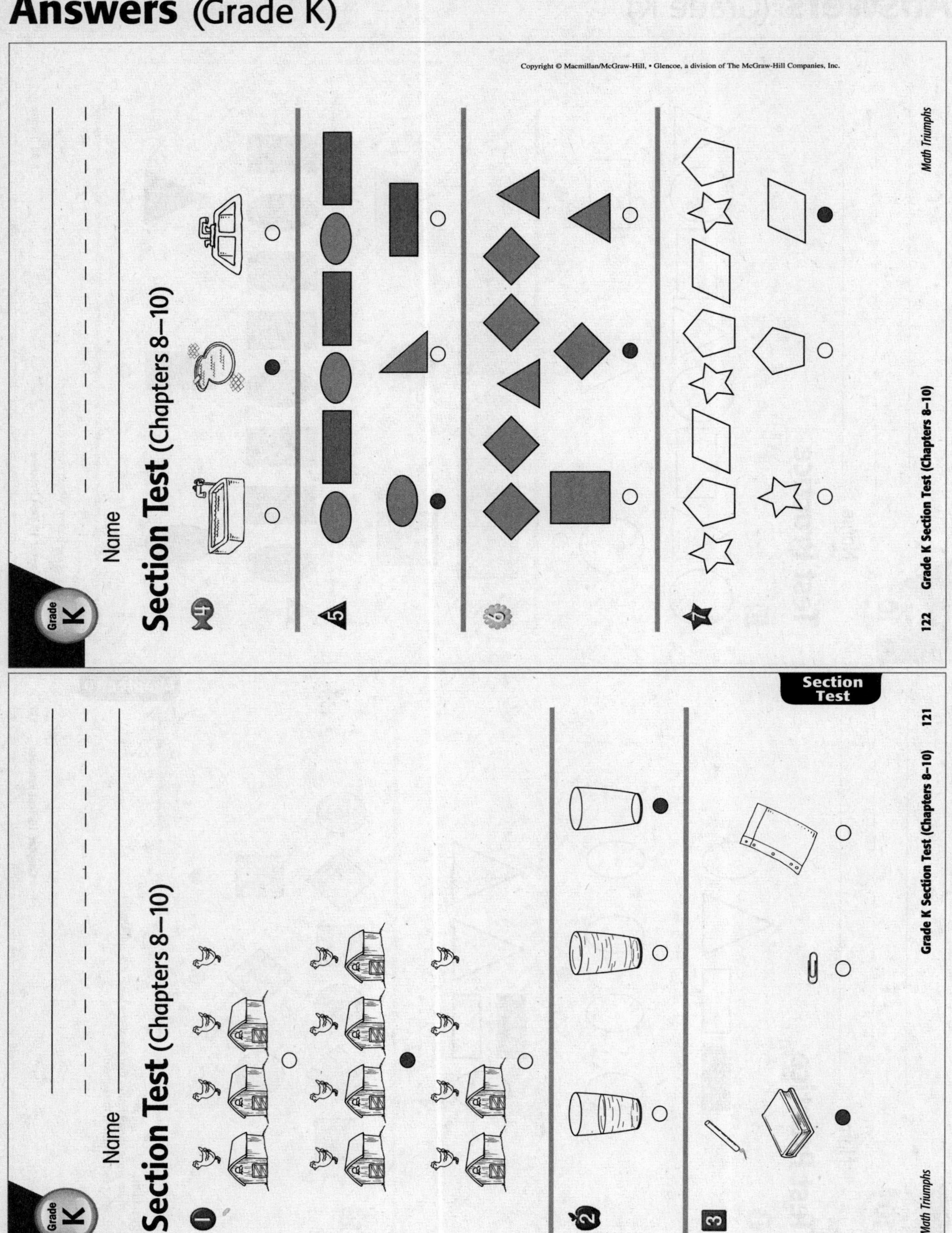

Name ______________ Date ________

Diagnostic and Placement Test

This test contains 15 questions. Work each problem in the space on this page. Select the best answer. Write the answer as directed.

1 Count the apples. Write the number. 7

2 Put an X on the set of four cherries.

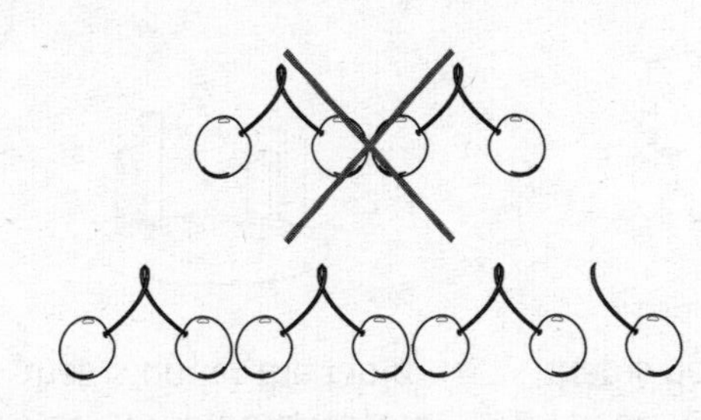

3 Circle the problem that fits the story. $2 + 1 = 3$

$\begin{array}{r} 2 \\ -\ 1 \\ \hline 1 \end{array}$ $\begin{array}{r} 2 \\ +\ 1 \\ \hline 3 \end{array}$

4 Look at the first square. Circle the squares that are the same size.

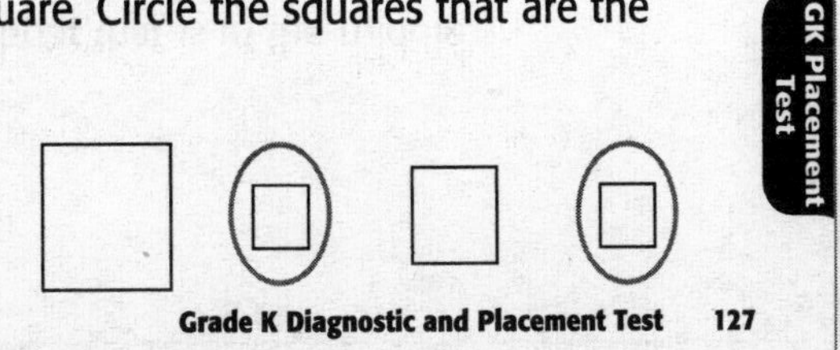

GK Placement Test

5 Circle the shape that comes next.

6 Look at the pattern. Circle the part that repeats.

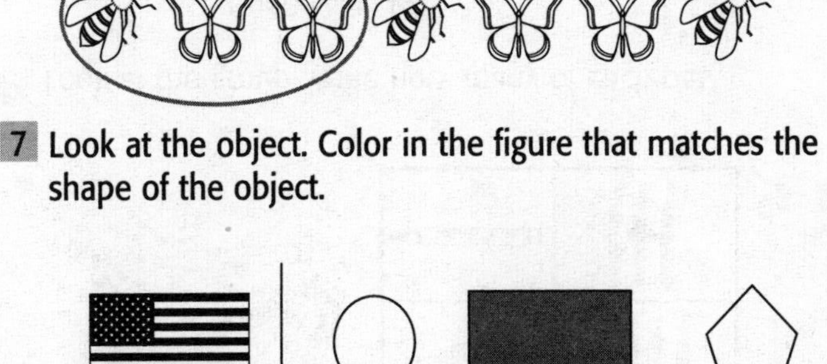

7 Look at the object. Color in the figure that matches the shape of the object.

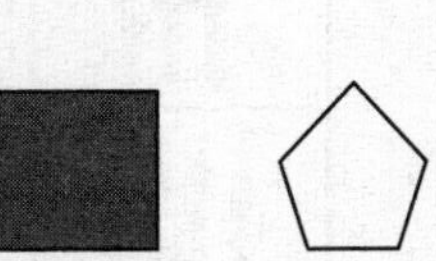

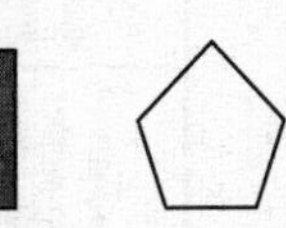

8 Put an X on the objects that can stack.

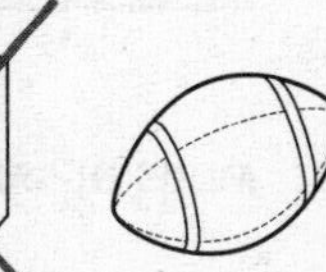

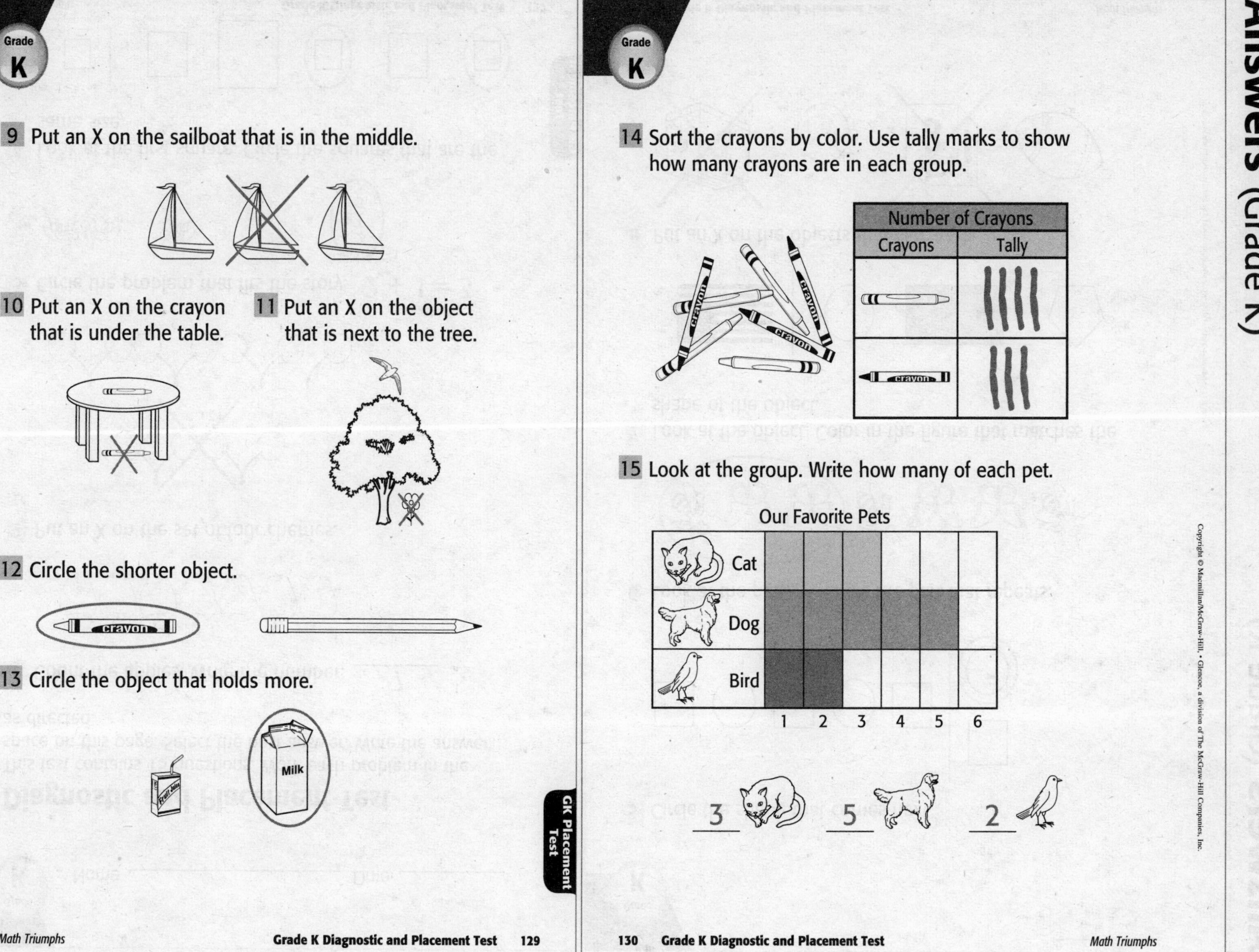

Grade K

9 Put an X on the sailboat that is in the middle.

10 Put an X on the crayon that is under the table.

11 Put an X on the object that is next to the tree.

12 Circle the shorter object.

13 Circle the object that holds more.

GK Placement Test

Grade K

14 Sort the crayons by color. Use tally marks to show how many crayons are in each group.

Number of Crayons	
Crayons	Tally
(white crayon)	||||
(dark crayon)	|||

15 Look at the group. Write how many of each pet.